BURNING LANDS AND SNOW-CAPPED MOUNTAINS

THE STORY OF THE TROPICS

BURNING LANDS
AND SNOW-CAPPED
MOUNTAINS

THE STORY OF THE TROPICS

Title II

by R. FRANK, JR.

ILLUSTRATED WITH PHOTOGRAPHS

THOMAS Y. CROWELL COMPANY · NEW YORK

BY THE AUTHOR

WORK BOATS

EXPERIMENTAL PLANES: Subsonic and Supersonic

ICE ISLAND: The Story of Antarctica

FLASHING HARPOONS: The Story of Whales and Whaling

FROZEN FRONTIER: The Story of the Arctic

BURNING LANDS AND SNOW-CAPPED MOUNTAINS:
    The Story of the Tropics

The photograph on the front of the jacket is used
through the courtesy of the South African Tourist Corp.
The photographs on the title page and on the back of the jacket
are used through the courtesy of the World Health Organization.

For Laura

Devoted Champion of All My Endeavors

CONTENTS

1

SIXTY-EIGHT DEGREES
AND RAINING

MOST OF US think of the tropics as a region of blazing sunshine, smothering heat, and torrential rainfalls. Generally, this is true. Yet almost every climate variation in the world may be found in the tropics—desert, temperate, and even a touch of arctic. Snow-capped mountains and glaciers exist on the equator.

The tropic, or torrid, zone is one of the five distinct climate zones into which the earth's surface is divided and whose limits are usually based on latitude. The torrid zone has its northern boundary at the Tropic of Cancer and its southern boundary at the Tropic of Capricorn; or latitude 23 degrees 27 minutes north and latitude 23 degrees 27 minutes south. These are the northernmost and southernmost points reached by the sun on its seasonal travels. Running through the middle of the tropics, like an imaginary line around a ball, is the equator.

This description is sufficient for most people. But scientists prefer a more accurate one. They define the tropics as those lands or regions where the average monthly temperature is

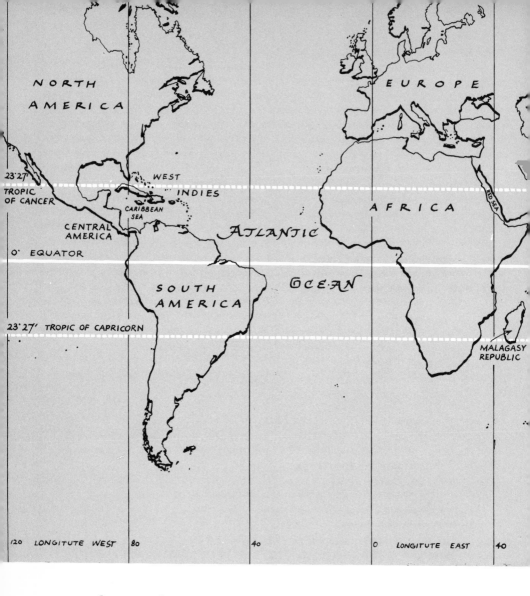

NORTH AMERICA

EUROPE

23°27'
TROPIC
OF CANCER

WEST INDIES

CARIBBEAN SEA

CENTRAL AMERICA

0° EQUATOR

ATLANTIC

AFRICA

RED SEA

SOUTH AMERICA

OCEAN

MALAGASY REPUBLIC

23°27' TROPIC OF CAPRICORN

120 LONGITUDE WEST 80

40

0 LONGITUDE EAST 40

at least 68 degrees F. This definition changes the north and south boundaries from straight lines to up-and-down curves.

But whatever definition is used, the tropics embrace a huge portion of our planet. Taken by geographical regions, the zone includes large areas of central Africa, much of southeast Asia, all of the Indonesian archipelago, Oceania, part of South America, practically all of Central America, and the

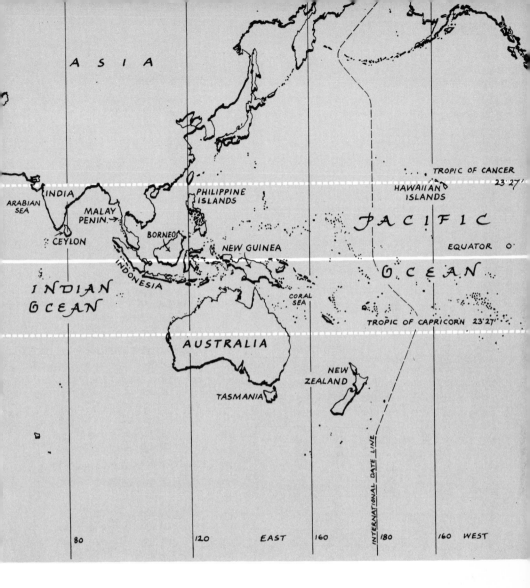

ASIA

INDIA
ARABIAN SEA
CEYLON
MALAY PENIN.→
BORNEO
INDONESIA

PHILIPPINE ISLANDS

NEW GUINEA

HAWAIIAN ISLANDS

PACIFIC

TROPIC OF CANCER
23° 27'

EQUATOR   0°

OCEAN

INDIAN OCEAN

CORAL SEA

TROPIC OF CAPRICORN 23° 27'

AUSTRALIA

TASMANIA

NEW ZEALAND

INTERNATIONAL DATE LINE

80   120   EAST   160   180   160   WEST

islands of the Caribbean Sea. In land area the tropics are estimated to cover 14.5 million square miles, four times the size of the United States.

A region so vast contains some of the most unusual and strangely contrasting features on the face of the earth. There are tropics that are dense rain-soaked forests, a shadowy, wet realm, where the sun rarely penetrates. This is the tropical

A roadway cutting through dense tropical forest.

jungle. It lies close to the equator and includes the Amazon basin in South America, the Congo basin in Africa, Malaya in southeast Asia, and most of the islands of the Indonesian archipelago.

In sharp contrast to the rain forests are the desert tropics, areas that are seared by scorching sun and hot, dry winds, where for months at a time no rain falls. These desert regions are, for example, in Africa, where small portions of the Sahara extend into the tropical zone, and in northern Chile. Semi-arid conditions also exist in many places from the 20th to the 25th parallels, both north and south of the equator, in tropi-

A jungle river in the Federation of Malaya.
Embassy of the Federation of Malaya

cal Africa (other than the Sahara), Asia, Australia, South and Central America.

There are high mountains in Africa, the islands of the Republic of Indonesia, Borneo, the Philippines, New Guinea, southeast Asia, and South America. Snow-capped Kilimanjaro in Tanganyika, Africa, rising to a height of 19,321 feet, is the most impressive mountain in the tropics. Several glaciers are slowly working their way down its towering slopes. A popular setting for adventure stories, Kilimanjaro has appeared in the tales of a number of modern writers. Ernest

These snow-capped mountains are not the Alps but towering summits in the Congo.

Belgian Government
Information Center

Hemingway, one of America's best known novelists, used the mountain as a background for *The Snows of Kilimanjaro*.

Many of the mountains, especially those on the islands of the Indonesian archipelago, are active volcanoes. One of the most devastating volcanic eruptions ever recorded took place in Indonesia in August of 1883 when the tiny island of Krakatoa blew up. The blast formed a submarine crater more than 1,000 feet deep.

The effects of Krakatoa's eruption were felt throughout the world. The explosion was heard 2,500 miles away. Ashes and other debris, shot to a height of 17 miles, were carried around the earth by air currents. Tidal waves 50 feet high were created and swept over the shores of nearby islands. The catastrophe destroyed entire towns and villages and took the lives of more than 36,000 people.

Giant landslides, called "lahars," are another danger in these mountains. Lahars occur when eruptions are accompanied by heavy rains and seas of volcanic substance, mud, and rock ooze down the mountain, swallowing everything in their path.

To forestall such disasters in Indonesia, an elaborate warning system has been set up. A series of lookout stations scattered throughout the active volcano area is manned by both human observers and instruments. Now, when volcanoes erupt and landslides threaten, the people living in the low-lying areas can be warned in time to leave.

These volcanoes, however, have a constructive as well as a destructive side. The tree-covered slopes catch rainwater and release it gradually to the numerous rivers flowing through the surrounding lowlands. The water is subsequently used for drinking and irrigating farms.

More important still, the volcanoes' frequent eruptions de-

Title II

A typical native shelter of Oceania is shown under construction. Women in foreground are drying copra, an important export.

with the formation of coral reefs on their foam-splashed shores.

Coral reefs are made of marine plants and animals that have attached themselves to land surfaces in shallow warm water. One of the most common of the reef builders is the coral polyp. This tiny sea creature fastens itself to the skeletons of preceding generations of animals and plants, and builds its own rocklike shell from the lime in the ocean water.

In a sense, Oceania is a pocket edition of all the topographical features to be found in the tropics. It has snow-capped mountains (central New Guinea), equatorial swamps, desert, and palm-fringed shores, the region's own contribution to the varied geography of the tropics, and finally, grassy savannas in Australia.

Oceania is composed of three giant island groups that stretch almost the entire width of the Pacific Ocean from the Hawaiian Islands to Australia and from the vicinity of Japan to New Zealand. The groups are divided into Melanesia, Polynesia, and Micronesia.

Melanesia, a word of Greek origin, means "black islands." They are so named because the natives inhabiting the islands are Negroids with an almost blue-black skin. The main islands in Melanesia are New Guinea, New Caledonia, Guadalcanal, and New Britain.

Polynesia means "many islands" in Greek. The word is derived from *polys* (many) and *neos* (island). Polynesia includes such far-ranging islands as New Zealand in the south, the Hawaiian Islands in the north, Easter Island in the extreme east, and Ellice and Samoa islands in the west.

Micronesia is the last of Oceania's great island complexes. The name, also of Greek origin, means "tiny islands." These hundreds of sea-washed specks, scattered over an area larger than the United States, are so small that the sum total of their land area is only about 1,260 square miles.

Micronesia is so vast and sprawling that it is generally divided into three island groups. These are the Marianas, the most northerly, the Carolines to the south, and finally, the Marshall and Gilbert Islands. Saipan and Tinian in the Marianas and Palau in the Carolines were the scene of some of the bitterest fighting in the Pacific during World War II.

Oceania is often referred to as an earthly paradise. In addition to the beauty of its many islands and seascapes,

The reflections of two Malayan farmers are mirrored at dusk in the rice paddies they have just worked.

Pacific Area Travel Association Photo

The outrigger canoe played an important role in the mass migrations of peoples throughout much of Oceania.

Oceania's balmy climate is one of the most delightful in the world. Artists, writers and others who wanted to get away from the unrelenting pressures of civilization have been drawn to the islands of the South Pacific to savor their beauty and solitude. Robert Louis Stevenson and Paul Gauguin, the French painter, were among those who felt that the breeze-

A mountain village in Tahiti.

swept tropical islands of Oceania were refreshing sanctuaries.

Climate, of course, distinguishes the tropics as a whole and not Oceania alone. A relatively high average temperature is one of several factors contributing to the uniqueness of the region's over-all climate. Weather experts have placed this at 68 degrees F. Furthermore, monthly temperature range throughout the tropics is slight, about 10 degrees F. In many areas, particularly over the oceans, it is less than 5 degrees F. Often the daily temperature change is greater than the yearly variation. The least variation in temperature occurs in the equatorial zone, a band 10 degrees north and south of the equator. As one moves toward the Tropic of Cancer and the Tropic of Capricorn, temperature range increases slightly. By way of contrast, New York City in the cooler months of the year may experience mercury fluctuations of 20 degrees or more in a 24-hour period. The warmest temperatures are recorded in a zone paralleling latitude 10 degrees north and not at the equator as it is popularly believed.

Rainfall is another unusual feature of the tropics' climate. Unlike the temperate zone, periodic rainfall and its absence mark the seasonal changes in the tropics. The heaviest and most frequent rains fall in the equatorial zone. This region as a rule experiences two rainy and two dry seasons a year. Some of the heaviest rains in the world occur here, which annually averages about 100 inches. A few rain-soaked localities that help make this figure possible are in parts of New Guinea with 369 inches and portions of equatorial Burma with more than 226 inches.

That portion of the tropics above the 10th parallel has but one wet and one dry season a year, or summer and winter respectively. Weather experts call this the tropical type of rainfall. Since winds play a key role in the arrival and departure of the rains, the wet and dry periods vary throughout the tropical zone. Thus in some areas of Africa the wet season may run from May through August. The dry season may extend from December through March. In tropical America, above the equator, the rains in some places may come in May and run through October. Below the equator they may arrive in October and extend through April.

Rainfall in the tropics is closely associated not only with climate, but also with the growth of vegetation and the living habits of the people. The tropical rain forests owe their existence to continuous high temperatures as well as excessive rainfall. The densest rain forests are found in the equatorial zone. The inhabitants' economic, agricultural, and social activities are geared to rainy and dry seasons.

Much of the rainfall comes with thunderstorms. Indeed, the tropics are said to experience more thunderstorms than any other place in the world. They usually are brief but intense. Sometimes six inches of rain will fall within a few hours. Many of the storms take place in the afternoon and are quickly followed by clear, sunny skies.

Winds are the third main element in the climate of the tropics. They have a Jekyll-and-Hyde nature, bringing benefit as well as harm. Trade winds are the "good" winds. Above the equator they are called northeast trade winds and are generally found in a zone from 10 degrees N. latitude to 30 degrees N. latitude. Between this band and the equator are the doldrums, a relatively calm region. Below the equator the winds are known as the southeast trade winds and range from the equator to about 25 degrees S. latitude.

The trade winds blow with extreme regularity and are refreshingly cool. People living in the path of these winds consider them a gift from heaven. With certain exceptions, their steady, regular flow brings a bracing coolness to the hot land. They not only help to regulate tropical temperatures, but they help to stabilize weather generally. The climate of the ocean areas over which trade winds blow is the least complicated and most even in the world. It is largely because of the trade winds that the climate of the South Sea islands is idyllic.

In the days of sailing vessels, trade winds played an important part in navigation. Once within the steady grip of these winds, a captain could count on a fast, comfortable voyage. But if caught in the doldrums, he fretted and fumed over his vessel's slow progress. Then the captain and crew experienced many uncomfortable days and night in the tropical heat.

Other times tropical winds may bring a storm that will work itself into a frightening fury. These are the "bad" winds. Few places in the world can boast storms of such violence. In the western Atlantic Ocean, these storms are known as hurricanes. In the Pacific, they are called typhoons. Both can cause great destruction.

Typhoons and hurricanes are torrential rains with winds of titanic force. They are normally 50 to 100 miles wide, but they have been known to reach 500 miles in width. Their winds have been clocked up to 200 miles per hour.

Even the United States Navy has known the awesome power of typhoons. During World War II a squadron of destroyers was steaming toward a battle area when the ships ran into a howling typhoon. Winds, clocked at more than 150 miles per hour, whipped the ocean into waves 100 feet high. Destroyers were tossed about like toy boats, pitching and listing to dangerous angles. Three of the vessels, unable to cope with the storm's fury, capsized and sank, carrying close to a thousand seamen to death.

In the fall of 1962 Typhoon Karen roared out of the South Pacific to batter the island of Guam with winds of more than 170 miles per hour. Homes and buildings believed to be typhoon-proof were flattened like kindling wood. More than 90 per cent of the island's dwellings were destroyed.

The inhabitants of the Gulf and Atlantic coast regions of the United States dread the violence and destruction of tropical storms. Annually one or more hurricanes sweep out of the tropics to batter them, leaving great property damage behind.

To minimize the destructiveness of these storms as much as possible, the United States government maintains a hurricane patrol operated jointly by the Weather Bureau, the Navy, and the Air Force. Radar-equipped aircraft go into action at the first sign that a hurricane is brewing in the Caribbean. The storm is kept under constant radar watch, its intensity and movement closely charted. Man-made satellites, which can survey enormous expanses of the earth's surface, are also being used for hurricane and typhoon watching.

Very often the climate of the tropics is summed up in one word—monotonous. In reality this is not quite true. There are areas in the torrid zone with distinct, varied climates of their own. Desert climate is one and may be found in different localities along the northern and southern boundaries of the tropics. True arid conditions exist in the tropics in northern Chile and the center of the Sahara. Semiarid areas with slightly more rainfall and varied plant life are in tropical America, Africa, and Australia.

In tropical desert climate rainfall is so haphazard that a

year may pass without a drop falling. In the desert of northern Chile the dry dusty soil is sprinkled with an average annual rainfall of 0.2 of an inch. Portions of the Sahara can boast of considerably better moisture conditions with as much as 7 inches falling in the course of a year. Plant life is scarce and of poor growth in these desert zones.

Another characteristic that marks the tropical desert climate is extreme heat. Indeed, areas with this climate can experience some of the highest temperatures of the torrid zone. In several desert localities temperatures of more than 122 degrees F. in the shade have been recorded. But, contrary to popular belief, the highest temperatures have not been recorded in the tropics but in the temperate zone.

Towering mountains are responsible for another of the tropics' different climate areas. Mountain climate, as it is

A snow-capped mountain in tropical East Africa.
Twentieth Century Fund

called, may be found in equatorial Africa, tropical America, southeast Asia, and even Oceania in New Guinea. Actually, in these mountainous localities it is possible to pass through several climate zones in a short time. One can travel up the mountain slopes from steaming lowlands through a temperate belt to near arctic conditions with snow and glaciers at the top. The plant life en route also shows remarkable variation, ranging from palm and banana trees to alpine flowers.

In the course of climbing a tropical mountain, for every 300 feet of elevation there is a temperature drop of 1 de-

The islands of Oceania offer a variety of landscape features—from low-lying, sandy atolls to forest-covered mountainous terrain.

gree F. It is interesting to note also that such a journey is like traveling away from the equator. Every 328 feet of elevation is equal to 93 miles in the direction of the north or south pole.

People living in the mountain climate do not feel that they are in the tropics at all. The temperature here is, for the most part, cool and pleasant. Bogotá, Colombia, and Quito, Ecuador, two cities close to the equator but at altitudes of 8,500 and 9,000 feet respectively, have an invigorating average temperature of about 57 degrees F.

In contrast to the mountainous areas, there are others with a monsoon climate. In these distinct zones the rainy and dry seasons coincide with periodic shifts in the prevailing wind. Thus, in parts of India when the southwest winds arrive in April and continue to blow through October, torrential rains fall with extreme regularity. As October draws to an end, the winds shift to the northeast, signaling the beginning of a dry season that lasts until April.

Other zones in the tropics with a monsoon climate are in southeast Asia, Indonesia, northern Australia, and west Africa.

Not only is there diversity in the climate of the tropics, there is even more diversity among its inhabitants and animal and plant life and in its history. All these combined make the tropics one of the most fascinating regions on earth.

2

EXPLORERS
EXPLODE A MYTH

UNTIL THE MIDDLE of the fifteenth century, the beliefs Europeans had concerning the tropics were based mostly on myths. For centuries they were certain that the tropics were unlivable. A popular conception was that anyone sailing to the torrid zone could expect to burn to death under a broiling sun or fall into a steaming hole in the ocean.

Many of the strange concepts which the Europeans held came from the Greeks who thought that the tropics were too hot to sustain human life. They were convinced of this even though Herodotus, one of their most famous historians, wrote about the experiences of travelers who had gone into the tropics and returned safely.

If the Greeks believed the tropics were unsuited for man, the Phoenicians certainly felt otherwise. These Mediterranean people were far-ranging sea rovers, constantly seeking new sources of trade. After exhausting the possibilities in the Mediterranean region, they sailed their ships through the Pillars of Hercules (Gibraltar) into the sea beyond. During the course of these ocean voyages the Phoenicians are believed to have entered the torrid zone. There is evidence that they sailed far down the coast of West Africa. They may even have rounded the Cape of Good Hope and penetrated the seas off eastern Africa. The Phoenicians were not given to boasting of their sea exploits, mainly because they feared the information might be helpful to commercial rivals. As a result of their secretiveness, historians have had a difficult time pinpointing the actual achievements of these daring sailors.

Historians, however, have had no such problem marking the beginning of Europe's interest in the tropics. It had its start in the early fifteenth century and the man mainly responsible was Prince Henry of Portugal. Because he initiated many sea voyages into unknown parts of the world, he became known as Prince Henry the Navigator.

Inspired by a keen interest in geography and a strong desire to expand the commercial activities of the Portuguese royal family, Prince Henry began the first European invasion of the tropics. For centuries the Portuguese, like most of their fellow Europeans, had restricted their travels to the continent. But in the Middle Ages scholars and merchants became more and more curious to know

l'Infant Don Henri.

Henry the Navigator of Portugal launched the first European exploring expeditions to the tropics.

what lay beyond their limited horizons. Prince Henry, more than most, had this curiosity.

Under his direction and encouragement a number of expeditions put to sea. Guiding their lumbering little caravels through the green Atlantic swells, Portuguese mariners cautiously poked their way south along Africa's northwest coast and west to the Azores. As each of the ships that had gone southward penetrated deeper and deeper into the tropics, and the seamen returned unharmed to talk about their adventures, the popular beliefs about the dangers of the tropics came to be questioned.

In 1433 the first of the Portuguese explorers ventured beyond Cape Bojador, Africa, the northern edge of the tropics. Encouraged by this success, Prince Henry's explorers in a few years pushed close to Cape Blanco, about 200 miles within the torrid zone.

Prince Henry did not live long enough to see his major goal—a crossing of the equator—achieved. But on the strength

Ships like these carried early European explorers to all corners of the tropics.

of the southward journeys that were accomplished in his lifetime, he was convinced that a man could survive in the so-called "burning zone." As the Portuguese explorers sailed their small ships farther and farther south, they suffered no harm from the sun. In fact, they reported the heat to be no worse than the hottest days of Portugal's summer.

The spirit of curiosity and daring which Prince Henry inspired in Portuguese mariners continued long after his death in 1460. For many years a parade of explorers left the ports of Portugal for the mysterious tropics. Outstanding among them was Diogo Cam, one of the first men to cross the equator. During his voyage of 1482–1484, Cam not only sailed farther south along Africa's west coast than any one had sailed before, to the 22nd parallel below the equator, but he also discovered the mouth of the Congo River. There he erected a stone to mark his discovery. Fragments of it still remain.

Bartholomew Diaz was another noted Portuguese explorer. Commanding a fleet of three ships, Diaz left Lisbon in 1487 to continue the trail pioneered by Diogo Cam. He sailed down Africa's west coast, rounded the southern tip, and headed up the eastern coast before turning back. On the homeward journey Diaz passed the Cape of Good Hope. Because he did not know that this was Africa's southernmost extremity, he is not generally credited with the Cape's discovery. This honor is usually given to Vasco da Gama, who in a few short years was to become even more famous than Diaz.

Da Gama got his start as an explorer under the Portuguese king Emanuel I. The monarch sent da Gama on a voyage of exploration with two main objectives. The first was to find a practical sea route to the East Indies, a region highly coveted by European kings and traders for its great riches in spices and silks. The second objective was to locate the fabled Prester John, who was believed to be the ruler of a fabulously rich land in central Africa.

In 1497, with a fleet of four ships and with Diaz as his pilot, Vasco da Gama began his voyage. He sailed southward and stopped first at the Cape Verde Islands. Then he headed west, coming within six hundred miles of the Brazilian coast. After this he swung his ships to the east and eventually reached the coast of Africa, at St. Helena Bay not far from the 33rd parallel. Da Gama then led his fleet around the Cape of Good Hope and pushed deep into the Indian Ocean, making port at Calicut on India's southwestern coast.

Da Gama did not reach the East Indies on this voyage nor did he find Prester John. But his observations and experiences helped to put an end to many of the strange ideas Europeans had about the tropics.

By 1510 a Portuguese fleet under an explorer named Affonso de Albuquerque had made its way as far as the East Indies. Albuquerque first captured Goa, a tiny settlement at India's southern tip, which was to remain a Portuguese possession until 1961. The Portuguese also took control of Malacca on the Malay Peninsula and then went on to the East Indies to establish commercial outposts there.

When word of the achievements of the Portuguese explorers spread throughout Europe, they aroused great interest, especially among the royalty and merchants of Spain, Holland, and England. As a result it was not long before ships of these nations were sailing tropical waters with the Portuguese. As Europeans began invading the tropics, they glimpsed a lush, green part of the earth unlike anything in their native lands. It was an exotic world which they believed contained great riches. They were surprised to find that certain areas were inhabited by highly civilized peoples, the Aztecs, Mayans, and Incas of North and South America, and the varied tribes of southeast Asia and Indonesia.

Christopher Columbus was among the explorers who were lured by the promise of riches in tropical lands. This Italian mariner sailed the unknown seas for the Spanish queen Isabella. Unlike the Portuguese, Columbus headed west on the broad Atlantic instead of south. After many days of bucking the ocean swells, he discovered the West Indies and the land that was subsequently to be called Central America.

Columbus made a total of four voyages to the New World, all of them to the tropics. His deepest penetration of this region took place during his third journey in 1498, when he landed at the mouth of the Orinoco River in South America. In 1502 Columbus's fourth and last voyage brought him close to the Isthmus of Panama where he sought a westward passage to the Orient.

In the wake of Columbus came a small army of Spanish adventurers who journeyed through many of the islands of the Caribbean, Mexico, Central America, and much of tropical South America. They looked not only for personal glory and riches, but also new lands and wealth for their king. They were equally anxious to spread Christianity among the natives of the new-found lands. Outstanding among the Spanish explorers were Hernando Cortez, who first met and conquered the Aztecs of Mexico; Balboa, who after crossing the Isthmus of Panama was the first European to see the waters of the Pacific Ocean; and Pizarro, perhaps the most adventurous of all. With a handful of soldiers he invaded the tropical portion of South America. After a tiring march through the hot lowlands, then on up to the chilly heights of the Andes Mountains, Pizarro conquered the sprawling empire of the Incas.

Most ambitious of the Spanish explorers, however, was Ferdinand Magellan. Magellan was a Portuguese by birth, but after failing to interest his king in a plan to sail around the world, he took his project to Spain where it was warmly received.

Ferdinand Magellan.

By the time Magellan began his explorations, many of the unknown parts of the earth had been discovered. But he felt there was still much for explorers to do. Some people continued to believe that the earth was flat and he wished to prove them wrong by voyaging around it.

In the course of his historic three-year voyage, Magellan sailed through vast areas of the tropics. Among his major discoveries were the Mariana Islands and the Philippines. Unfortunately he lost his life on Mactan Island in the Philippines when, in a fight with the natives, he was run through with a spear and killed. Following Magellan's death, the surviving expedition members prepared to continue their voyage after first burning the worst of the leaking ships. They left the Philippines aboard the two remaining vessels, the *Trinidad* and the *Victoria*. But the *Trinidad* also became unseaworthy and had to be abandoned. The *Victoria* after many weary months reached Spain in September of 1522. The crew was the first ever to circumnavigate the globe.

The death of Magellan.

Although the Spaniards played a large role in the drama of discovering the tropics, the Dutch were almost as active. Unlike the Spaniards, however, the explorers from Holland were more interested in finding new lands for trading purposes than in enriching the treasury of their king or in spreading Christianity. In the course of carrying out their objec-

The Victoria, *the first ship to sail around the world and the only one of Magellan's fleet to survive the voyage.*

tives, they confined their explorations almost wholly to the spice-rich islands of the East Indies.

A driving force behind the exploits of Dutch explorers was the Dutch East India Company. This was a group of rich merchants who, with the blessings of the Dutch king, had banded together for the purpose of seeking, taking possession of, and developing islands in the East Indies. The Company had the sole trading rights in any newly discovered land, as well as the exclusive right to send ships to the Far East. In other words, no Dutchman outside the small circle of wealthy merchants who made up the East India Company was allowed to engage in trade with the Indies.

Among the Dutch explorers in the Pacific were Cornelius Houtman, first to lead a Dutch expedition from Holland to Java in 1595; William Schouten, who found the Hoorn Islands; and Abel Tasman, discoverer of New Zealand and Tonga, who sailed around southern Australia.

By the early 1600's the Dutch had sent thirteen expeditions to the East Indies, which eventually gave them a long-lasting foothold in the region. Their influence was further strengthened in 1619 when Jan Pieterszoon Coen captured Jakarta, Java, and obtained valuable commercial privileges from the native princes on neighboring Sumatra. Indeed, the Dutch in time became so powerfully entrenched in the Indies, mainly on Java and Sumatra, that for years the islands were known as the Dutch East Indies.

The English were also tireless explorers of the Pacific tropics. During the first half of the eighteenth century, they completed the discovery of all the major islands in Polynesia. Explorers such as Commodore John Byron, Samuel Wallis, and Philip Carteret sailed over thousands of miles of uncharted seas to discover such islands as Tahiti, Uvea, and parts of the Tuamotu archipelago in the south Pacific.

But the explorer who outshone all the others was Captain James Cook of the British Royal Navy. As the result of three remarkable voyages, he revealed almost all of the world of the south Pacific. On his first expedition (1768–1771), Captain Cook discovered the islands of Huahine, Raiatea, Tahaa, Bora Bora and Rurutu. He also spent many weeks surveying the coasts of New Zealand and New Guinea, as well as the east coast of Australia.

Captain Cook's second voyage lasted three years (1772–1775) and took him completely around the world. His main objective was to find a huge southern continent believed to exist in the Antarctic. Blocked time and again by an impenetrable ice barrier, he finally acknowledged defeat and decided to head for the south Pacific. Here Captain Cook again identified a number of new islands—Fatu Hiva, Palmerston, New Caledonia, Norfolk, and the Hervey Islands.

Captain Cook landing on the island of Tonga.

Captain Cook's third and final visit (1776–1779) to the Pacific, during which he surveyed the North American coast, led to the finding of Mangaia, Atiu, Tubuai, the Christmas Islands, and, most important of all, the Hawaiian Islands, which he called the Sandwich Islands. Although there is evidence that the Hawaiian Islands were visited a century and a half earlier by a Spanish mariner, Juan Gaetano, most historians give Cook the credit for the discovery.

The Hawaiian Islands marked the end of Captain Cook's brilliant career. The explorer and his men became embroiled with the natives over some stolen ship's property. Harsh words were followed by a brief, fierce scuffle in which Captain Cook was killed. The struggle took place on the big island of Hawaii and it was here that the British explorer's remains were buried.

This lighthouse, built in 1867, marks the spot where Captain Cook came ashore on the island of Tahiti in 1769.

Perhaps the most extraordinary explorations of all in tropical Oceania were undertaken not by Europeans but by Polynesians. Crowding women, children, food, pigs, chickens, seeds, plants, and household belongings into small but fast outrigger canoes, Polynesians set out over the trackless Pacific for new island homes. Their ability to pinpoint objectives without the help of navigating instruments remains an amazing achievement.

The Polynesians lived in an ocean world and they developed into remarkable mariners. Over countless generations they learned to use nature's signposts in their travels over the vast Pacific. They found their way by studying the movement and position of the stars, by observing the flight of birds, and gauging the direction of the wind. They carefully chose the right time of year to embark; when the winds were favorable, they set sail.

Although some of the voyages ended in disaster, when unexpected storms blew up and huge waves capsized the frail, overloaded canoes, other voyages were successful and led to the populating of many islands throughout Polynesia. These Polynesian sea journeys, compared by many historians with the early achievements of the Phoenicians and Vikings, are believed to have taken place over a span of several centuries, beginning about one thousand years ago, perhaps even earlier.

By the late eighteenth century, a new type of explorer was beginning to visit the tropical world. Scientists, primarily interested in the people, flora, and fauna made detailed studies of the tropics. Among the earliest and greatest of these was the German naturalist, Alexander von Humboldt. In the company of the French botanist, Aimé Bonpland, Humboldt came to the tropics in 1799 and remained for five years, concentrating his studies on plants and trees. During his travels he covered large areas of South America, particularly those parts through which the Amazon River and a tributary, the Rio Negro, loop and twist. Humboldt also journeyed through Cuba and Mexico.

When the naturalist returned to Europe with specimens of exotic plants and numerous stories of the strange sights to be seen in the tropics, he inspired other scientists to journey there. Humboldt himself had been encouraged to visit the American tropics by the written accounts of early Spanish explorers, especially those of Francisco de Orellana, who in 1541–1543 was the first white man to travel from the headwaters of the Amazon River to the Atlantic coast. De Orellana named the river and the region after a band of women warriors he met and called Amazons.

Several of the more noteworthy scientists who caught Humboldt's enthusiasm for the tropics were Charles Darwin, Alfred Wallace, and Henry Bates. It was in the tropics that Darwin did much of the field work which supported his theory of evolution. He journeyed through the torrid zone aboard *H. M. S. Beagle*, as the naturalist member of a British exploring expedition. Darwin left his native England on December 27, 1831 and did not return for five years. Among the many places he visited were Brazil and Tahiti.

Alfred Wallace and Henry Bates were naturalists who went to the region of the tropics together. They worked as a team for only a short time before going their separate ways. Wallace, following the turns and twists of the Amazon River, tramped through the tropical forests from 1848 to 1852. After pushing deep into Brazil's jungle domain, he returned to the coast by way of the Orinoco River. In the course of his journey he collected a vast number of plant and animal specimens. But a fire broke out aboard the ship on which he was returning to England and destroyed almost all of his scientific collection.

Henry Bates was a butterfly specialist. The Amazon River area is the home of such a wide variety of butterflies that Bates stayed for eleven years. He concentrated on the lower half of the Amazon valley and on his return to England wrote a comprehensive description of it.

Interest in the Amazon region did not end after the visits of eighteenth- and nineteenth-century naturalists. Explorer-scientists continued to find this part of the tropics fascinating. One of the better known of the twentieth-century explorers was Hamilton Rice, an American who made five exhaustive survey trips to the Amazonian tropics.

Colonel P. H. Fawcett, another American, explored the Mato Grosso uplands of Brazil. He continued his studies for many years, then in 1925 entered the tropical jungle for what proved to be his last visit. He mysteriously disappeared and no trace of him has ever been found.

Tropical Africa has held an equal attraction for the explorer-scientists. But these men are only a part of a larger group of explorers who went to Africa to see what mysteries the interior held. Some came purely for the love of adventure. Some were eager to claim possession of new lands for their governments. And finally there were the missionaries who sought to change the beliefs of the natives. Their travels and adventures make a monumental story, filled with color, drama, and courage.

The Jesuit missionaries in the fifteenth century were among the earliest white travelers to penetrate the African interior. They came primarily to establish contact with the people of Ethiopia (Abyssinia) who had first become Christians in the fourth century after Christ. Three hundred years later, when the Arabs ascended to power in northern Africa, the Ethiopians were cut off from their Christian colleagues. But they held on to their beliefs, despite long isolation and eventual Moslem conquest. Thus, when the missionaries entered the remote mountain stronghold, they found great numbers of Ethiopians still clinging to Christian ways.

Father Paez was outstanding among these missionary explorers. In 1613 he traveled widely through the highlands of Ethiopia, seeking the source of the Blue Nile, a branch of the mighty Nile River. He gathered a considerable amount of information, not the least of which concerned the Nile's periodic floodings. After some study he concluded that they were due to seasonal tropical rains and not to melting snows from nearby mountains as had been commonly believed.

In the mid-eighteenth century knowledge of tropical Africa was further increased by James Bruce, a Scotsman of considerable wealth. With time and money for study and travel, Bruce became fascinated with Africa. The geography of this continent was a favorite subject of discussion among scholars of his day. There was a particular curiosity concerning the sources of Africa's four largest rivers—the Nile, Niger, Zambesi, and Congo. It was primarily to find the source of the best known of these, the Nile, that Bruce went to Africa.

He started on his journey in 1768 and did not return to his native land until five years later. In the course of his long sojourn, Bruce experienced enough adventures to make several movie scenarios. He was forced to endure intense heat and violent storms. The explorer also had to overcome rugged terrain, and the often hostile attitude of natives. Once he was held captive by the friendly ruler of Ethiopia who liked the visitor so much that he made him a governor of one of the country's provinces. Although Bruce appreciated the king's friendship, he had no desire to be a governor. He had come to Africa for more important business and, despite the watchful eye placed upon him, was determined to carry out his original plan. As soon as Bruce could, he seized the chance to flee and made his way to Lake Tana in Ethiopia. After surveying the lake and the surrounding mountains, he became convinced that here was the main source of the Blue Nile.

Bruce used the river to make his escape from the interior of tropical Africa. After reaching home he wrote a vivid account of his adventures. The book stirred up so much interest that the Dark Continent became a favorite region for British explorers.

One result which Bruce's story helped to bring about in England was the creation in 1788 of the African Association, a forerunner of the Royal Geographical Society of London. The group was organized for two main purposes: to encourage exploration in Africa for the expansion of British commerce and to support political control over African lands.

Among the first explorers sent to Africa by the association was another Scot, a young doctor by the name of Mungo Park. His assignment was to find the mouth of the Niger River and the general direction in which it flowed. There was much controversy among geographers on this last point.

Park began his expedition on the upper reaches of the river and for two years, 1795–1797, struggled through dense forests to carry out his tasks. Time and again his life was in danger from hostile natives. Although he failed to locate the mouth of the Niger, Park did find that the river flowed mainly in an easterly direction. He also gained a vast amount of knowledge about the upper Niger region of tropical Africa.

In 1805 Park led another expedition into the African interior. Again his goal was to find the last meandering miles of the Niger. This time he traveled for the British Government, which had asked him to undertake the mission, but he was no more successful than before. While sailing down the Niger his boat became trapped among the rocks of a rapids. Exposed and helpless, he and his colleagues were attacked by natives from the river bank with spears and arrows. When they attempted to escape by swimming down the rushing river, Park and most of the expedition were drowned.

Not until 1830 was the mystery of the Niger's mouth made clear. Richard Lemon Lander and his brother, picking up the trail where Park met his death, followed the Niger to where it flowed into the Gulf of Guinea.

Througout the 1800's the exploration of tropical Africa's interior continued at an ever quicker tempo. And, as earlier English explorers continued to play a leading role. They were encouraged by the Royal Geographical Society which came into existence in 1830. The Society supported a number of expeditions to Africa; among the first was that led in 1857 by Sir Richard Burton and John Speke.

These two adventurers had hardly begun their explorations before it was necessary to split up. Burton became ill with fever while at Lake Tanganyika and had to remain there to recuperate. Speke, impatient over the delay, decided to push on alone for the north. Eventually, he discovered Africa's largest body of fresh water which he named Lake Victoria after the British queen. It was the major find of the expedition because it proved to be the principal source of water for the White Nile, the southern branch of the Nile River.

John Speke returned to tropical Africa in 1860, alone this time, and headed straight for the scene of his first triumph.

He was curious to know how Lake Victoria got its water. Speke obtained his answer with the discovery of the Kagera River. This achievement was doubly rewarding because the Kagera was also judged the true source of the Nile River.

While Speke was exploring the eastern inland portion of tropical Africa, another British expedition, headed by Samuel Baker and his wife, was tramping through the same region. The Bakers spent 1861 to 1865 in Africa. At the end of their journey they had two important achievements to their credit. One was the discovery of Lake Albert, the seventh largest lake in tropical Africa; the other the discovery of Murchison Falls.

This part of Africa was a favorite region for explorers in the mid-nineteenth century. But it was not the only part to attract them. The central and western portions were also being investigated, particularly by the most famous of all African explorers, Dr. David Livingstone.

This Englishman first acquired his interest in Africa and its people when he came in 1841 as a missionary. He was appalled by the cruelties of the slave trade, which was then at its height, and was seized by a strong desire to do what he could to stop the evil practice.

In the course of his one-man crusade Livingstone traveled over many square miles of tropical Africa's forest land and visited numerous tribes. After a few years in the steaming heat of the jungle, Livingstone felt that he could best realize his goals by exploring and opening up the interior of Africa. He became interested in exploring the unknown portions of the dark continent. This became the career to which he devoted thirty-two years of his life. With a keen sense of observation and considerable skill as a surveyor, Livingstone was well-equipped to carry out his new role. He was aided too, by the friendship of many African tribes who appreciated his efforts to aid them. The tribesmen helped him on his marches and guided him to a number of their landmarks.

Livingstone's first achievement as an explorer was his discovery of Lake Ngami in Bechuanaland on his expedition of 1849. Later, he discovered the magnificent Victoria Falls in Rhodesia, called by Africans "The Smoke That Thunders," and beautiful Lake Nyasa, in Tanganyika.

At one time in his exploring career Livingstone disappeared into the tropical jungle and was gone for seven years. Fearing for his safety, friends at home began to make efforts to locate him. In the course of this search another famous African explorer, Henry Morton Stanley, found Livingstone at Ujiji, on Lake Tanganyika, November 10, 1871. As the two adventurers met in the deepest part of equatorial Africa, Stanley uttered the now-famous words, "Dr. Livingstone, I presume?"

Livingstone was a tireless, meticulous explorer who literally gave his life to the task of illuminating the dark unknown of equatorial Africa. He carried on his surveys in later years even when he was so ill with dysentery that he had to be carried on a litter by his native helpers. The maps of his travels were made with such accuracy that even today his routes can be easily followed.

Dysentery eventually killed Dr. Livingstone. He died in a tiny village on the south edge of the vast swamp of Bangweulu in Rhodesia. By the time he entered the last note in his field book, he had traveled overland and by boat more than 30,000 miles and made a monumental contribution to our knowledge of the geography of tropical Africa. His body was sent home to England where it was buried, with honors, in Westminster Abbey.

Our account of African exploration would not be complete without some further mention of Henry Stanley, who was born in England and grew up in America. He embarked on a career in journalism and in the course of his newspaper work became deeply interested in Livingstone's explorations. When Livingstone was believed lost, Stanley was chosen by his newspaper, the *New York Herald,* to join the search for the English explorer. In this way Stanley caught the exploring fever; newspaper work thereafter became secondary.

Stanley began his explorations in Africa in 1874 in the vicinity of Lake Tanganyika, when he undertook his most important expedition. Starting in the eastern section of tropical Africa, near lakes Victoria and Tanganyika, he headed through bush and jungle for Africa's west coast.

Expecting trouble from hostile natives, Stanley started out with 200 heavily armed Europeans and Africans. By the time he reached the Atlantic coast the expedition had been reduced to two dozen men, the result of sickness and thirty-one battles with the natives. Later, when writing about his experiences, Stanley said that he had literally to fight his way across Africa.

His trans-continental march had taken him from Lake Tanganyika to the Lualaba River which he followed to the Congo River. He then traced the Congo's winding course to its mouth on the Atlantic coast. By his epic journey Stanley made extensive areas of central Africa known to the world. His fame became widespread.

While on his way back to America, Stanley was intercepted by an emissary from King Leopold II of Belgium with a request to head another expedition into equatorial Africa, this time for the Belgian government. Stanley agreed and for five years, beginning in 1879, he explored the Congo Basin.

Lake Tumba and Lake Leopold II were two of his discoveries. As a result of his work, the Congo Free State came into existence under the control of the Belgian government. Like many other African colonies, the Congo has since become free of foreign rule.

Stanley went back to Africa to explore for the last time in 1887. His stay was brief, however, and he accomplished little of importance.

Unlike Africa, the tropical world of southeast Asia and Oceania in the nineteenth century offered fewer opportunities to explorers for acquiring colonies or new geographical knowledge. Most of this kind of exploration had been completed in the previous century. But this part of the tropics had much to give to the scientist-explorer, especially the anthropologist and naturalist. Once this became known, scientist-explorers began visiting the region with more and more frequency. Foremost of these was Alfred Russel Wallace, a naturalist who had in earlier years spent a long period in the jungle of the Amazon.

Wallace came to the East Indies in 1854 and liked it so much that he remained for eight years. He wandered through the many islands of the archipelago, studying and collecting thousands of flora and fauna. As a result of his exhaustive investigations here and in the American tropics, Wallace formed a theory of evolution similar to Charles Darwin's. In fact, both theories were published in a joint paper by the Linnaean Society of London in 1858. Wallace also wrote a book on the animal and plant life of the East Indies which has become a classic.

Although the tropics have been explored as thoroughly as any other region on earth, men of an adventuresome mind, as well as scientific, are still moved to go there. There is little for them to discover, however, since only a few areas remain that have not been seen by the eyes of white men. These isolated pockets are largely in tropical America and on the island of New Guinea in the southwest Pacific. It is safe to assume that even these areas of isolation will soon be a thing of the past. The never-ending search for natural resources, if for no other reason, will see to that.

3

FROM DYAK
TO HOTTENTOT

MAN HAS BEEN LIVING in the tropics longer, perhaps, than in any other region on earth. Many anthropologists are of the opinion that the torrid zone was the incubator, so to speak, in which prehistoric man slowly evolved to his present form. In support of this theory they point to the numerous earliest types of prehistoric man that have been unearthed in the tropics.

The Java Man was one of the first primitive men to be discovered. Later, tropical Africa has been the scene for even more important anthropological finds such as Zinjanthropus or East Africa Man. Unearthed in 1959 by Dr. L. S. B. Leakey and his wife in Olduvai gorge, Tanganyika, this early ancestor of man is believed to have roamed central Africa. Leakey has estimated this bone fragment to be 1,750,000 years old but his figure has been disputed by some who feel the figure should be closer to 1,000,000. Not long after this discovery the remains of a man-like creature were found in Kenya by the same anthropological team. It has been estimated to be 14 million years old. As a result of these and other finds, Dr. Leakey is convinced that man originated in central Africa and later migrated to other continents.

This theory explains in part, perhaps, the fact that the tropics has a racial and cultural variety of peoples unmatched anywhere in the world. In the tropics are thousands of people still living in the Stone Age, as, for example, the aborigines of Australia. And there are millions of people as culturally advanced as any in the twentieth century. Between these cultural groups are countless inhabitants in various stages of

Women and children of India carrying water.
World Health Organization (Eric Schwab)

Peasants in a small village in southern India, leading their bullocks to water-holes.

The interior of a rich man's home in a village near Mysore, India.

World Health Organization
(Eric Schwab)

Below: A poor man's home in an Indian village. Peasants of this village have an average income per family unit of $200 a year.

World Health Organization
(Eric Schwab)

World Health Organization (Paul Almasy)

Adequate drinking water is a problem for Calcutta's teeming population. Water must often be carried home in pails and jars from public pumps.

social, economic, and political advancement. Many of these people are discarding the primitive ways of field and jungle for a more progressive life in towns and cities. They are attending schools, acquiring jobs in factories and mines, and learning the rules of self-government.

Storing grain in cool underground silos in India.

World Health Organization (Eric Schwab)

Southeast Asia and the East Indies offer a particularly varied tapestry of peoples and societies. Here one may find not only the earth's principal racial stocks—Negroid, Caucasoid, and Mongoloid—but others resulting from a mixture of these three.

The Shwedagon Pagoda in Rangoon, Burma.
World Health Organization

These government buildings of Moorish architecture in Kuala Lumpur, capital of the Federation of Malaya, reflect the influence of the peoples who migrated from India to this part of southeast Asia.

Long before the coming of the first Europeans, advanced civilizations flourished in Burma, Malaya, Laos, Cambodia, Vietnam, and portions of the East Indies. As early as the eighth century Malaya was the center of a mighty Buddhist empire. In the tenth century the Khmers were supreme in Cambodia and much of the surrounding region. A people of great artistic, architectural, and engineering skills, they created many splendors, some of which may still be seen in the magnificent ruins of Angkor, one-time capital of Cambodia. The city's carved stone temples and shrines rival in magnificence the artistic achievements of the ancient Mediterranean world.

While the ancient peoples of southeast Asia and the East Indies developed and generally maintained cultures that were uniquely their own, they did not escape the influence of outsiders, particularly the Indians and Chinese. Hindus from India brought a highly developed religion as well as forms of art, literature, and architecture. They were especially influential among the peoples of Sumatra and Java where evidence of their culture exists today.

The Chinese were an almost equally potent cultural force, making important contributions in the fields of religion and commerce. Even at present in many parts of southeast Asia and the East Indies they continue to exercise a strong influence. In Malaya (where they outnumber the local inhabitants) and in Thailand the Chinese play key roles in commerce, industry, and government.

Religion was one of the more lasting of the outside cultural influences. Buddhism and Hinduism were accepted

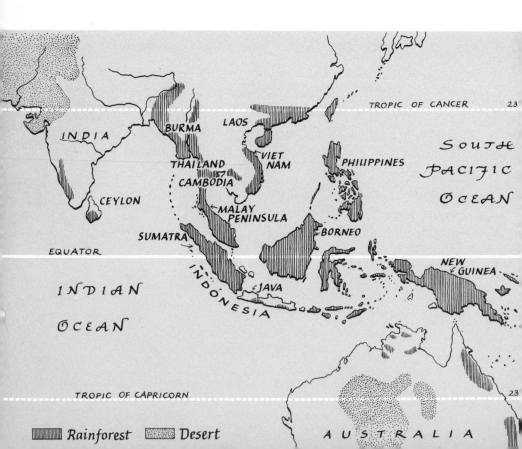

The Lamp, Standard Oil Co. (N.J.)

A canal on the outskirts of Bangkok. The cone-shaped structure on the right is a Buddhist shrine, called a stupa.

early, about the fifth century. Later, Hinduism, which flourished on Sumatra and Java, was largely replaced by Islam. Buddhism and Islam are today the two principal religions in this part of the tropics. Indonesia is the second largest Islamic country in the world.

In this modern age it is primarily the peoples with a rich historical and cultural past who are the most advanced in southeast Asia and Indonesia. Agriculture is their main occupation, just as it has been for centuries. Rice is the principal crop. Fishing is also a means of livelihood, as are the cultivating and tapping of rubber trees and the mining of tin.

This Thai woman, one foot held in position by a thong, is poling her craft laden with charcoal.

The Lamp, Standard Oil Co. (N.J.)

A school "bus" in Thailand.

The villages and towns are self-contained units where the inhabitants provide almost all their own needs. Besides being skilled farmers, they are often expert craftsmen. In such large, modern, bustling cities as Rangoon, Hanoi, Bangkok, Saigon, and Jakarta, people work and play as people do in the most sophisticated cities in the world.

Yet not far away are forest dwellers practically living in the Stone Age. Here men, isolated by rugged mountains or impenetrable swamps and jungles, follow a way of life little changed from that of their ancestors thousands of years ago. Many hunt their food and gather fruits and wild plants from the forests and fields. They practice primitive religious and social rites and only in recent years have they been persuaded to abandon head hunting.

This native Papuan boy wears bark strips plaited into his hair and shells for decoration.

The Ibans, who are considered to be Dyaks—a non-Muslim people of Borneo—are typical of these primitives. Not many years ago they were known to take heads. The Ibans have been discouraged from this practice. Today their farming supplies food once obtained from the forest.

Inhabited as it is by so many different groups, southeast Asia and Indonesia have a wide variety of languages. The number of different tongues literally outdoes the Biblical Tower of Babel. Despite this diversity, however, language experts have been able to distinguish four main types. Three

Primitive tribesmen of New Guinea.

of these, Tibeto-Burman, Siamese, and Annamese are confined mostly to the peoples of Burma, Thailand, and Indo-China.

The fourth great language group is called Malayo-Polynesian. It is spoken by most of the inhabitants of the region which stretches from Thailand and Malaya to the easternmost parts of Indonesia. In New Guinea and on some of the smaller islands nearby the natives speak an entirely different language, called Papuan.

The written language is also varied. It is based on four different alphabets, Arabic, Indian, Chinese, and Roman. The Arabic was introduced about seven hundred years ago with the Muslim religion. Before that, writing was based largely on

Indian and Chinese alphabets. When the Europeans came in the sixteenth century, they brought the Roman alphabet.

Throughout southeast Asia and the East Indies, the people are experiencing profound social and political changes. Since the days of the early European explorers much of the land has been under foreign control. Now the inhabitants are

Temple dancers of Thailand.

taking charge of their own political destinies. During the decades following World War II, a number of new countries were born and have joined the world family of nations.

On the mainland of Asia they include The Federation of Malaya, Burma, Laos, and South Vietnam. The Republic of Indonesia has replaced Dutch rule over almost all the East Indies. Among the islands forming this new republic are Sumatra, Java, Borneo (Kalimantan), Sulawesi (Celebes), the Lesser Sunda Islands, and the Moluccas.

In the vast tropical world of Oceania, the natives have long been of interest to anthropologists, who wonder about their origins. This is especially true of the inhabitants of Polynesia. Some scientists believe they hop-scotched across the Pacific from the Asian mainland and its off-shore islands many centuries ago. Dissenters, however, offer the unusual idea that these natives really came from South America.

Thor Heyerdahl, a strong advocate of the South American theory, tried to show how the Polynesians and their island neighbors might have migrated from South America. Sailing on a balsa wood raft, the *Kon-Tiki,* he voyaged from Peru to Easter Island, eastern outpost of the Polynesian Islands. The ocean journey was a remarkable personal achievement, but it failed to sway many anthropologists who, by and large, still hold to the idea that Asia was the natives' original home.

Whatever their origin, the inhabitants of Micronesia and Polynesia, basically distinct racial groups, have an extraordinary relationship with the sea. They are excellent boatmen, sailing their swift, frail outrigger canoes for long distances over the Pacific. And they are just as much at home in the water as upon it. Some are powerful, expert swimmers and have participated in the Olympic Games.

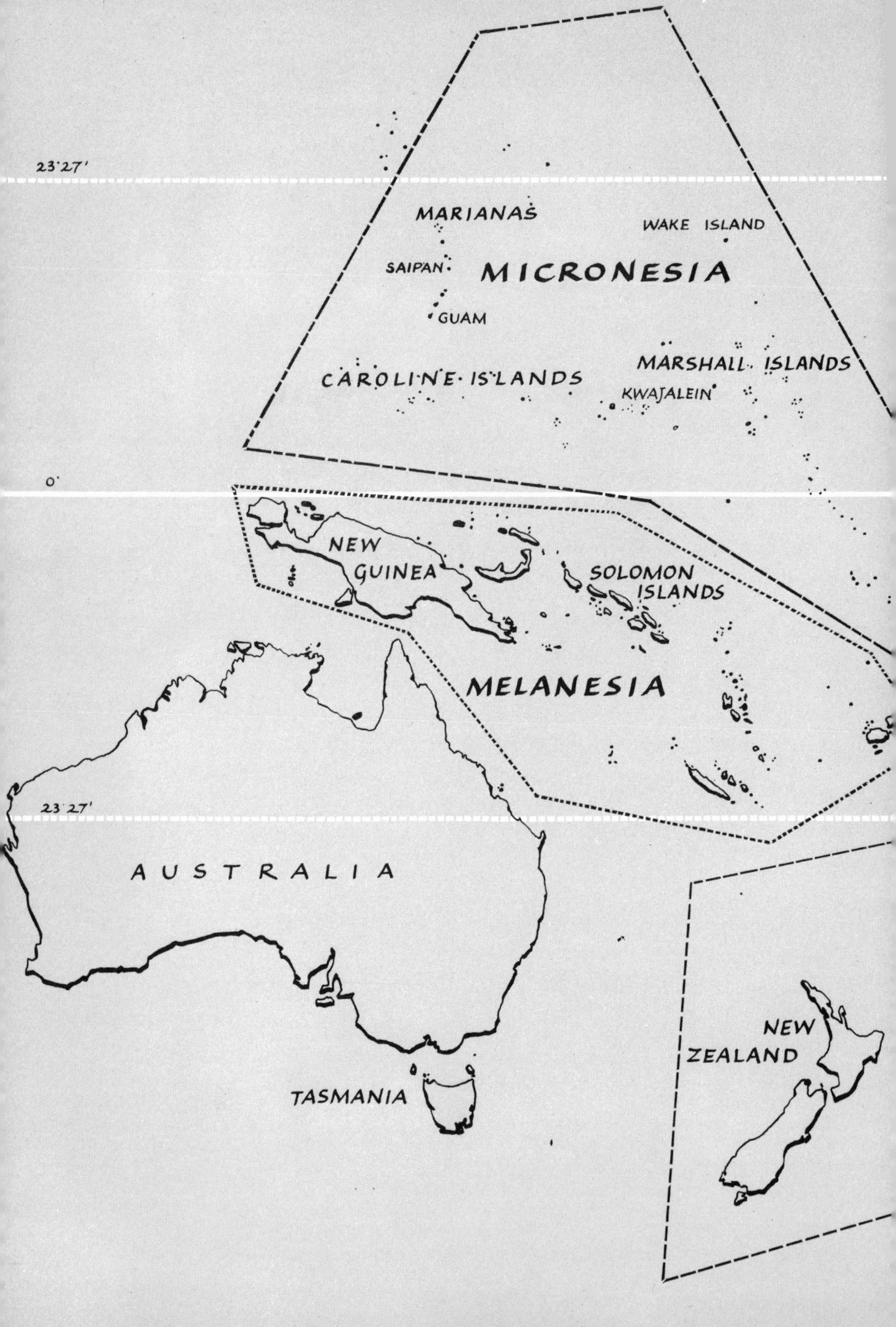

23°27'

MARIANAS   WAKE ISLAND

SAIPAN·   MICRONESIA

·GUAM

                                        MARSHALL ISLANDS
CAROLINE·ISLANDS   KWAJALEIN

0'

            NEW   SOLOMON
            GUINEA   ISLANDS

                        MELANESIA

23°27'

            AUSTRALIA

                                            NEW
                                        ZEALAND

            TASMANIA

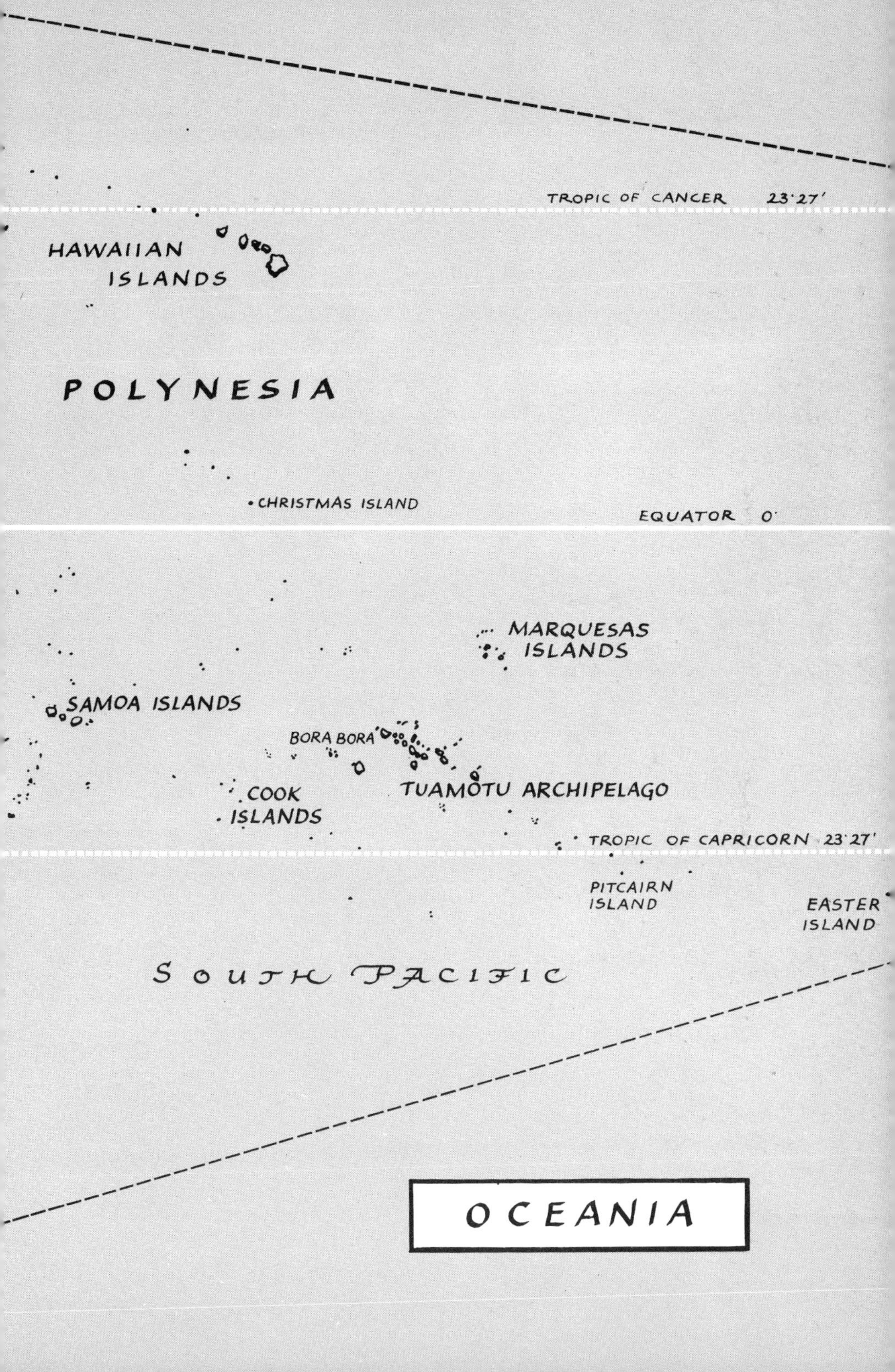

TROPIC OF CANCER   23°27'

HAWAIIAN
ISLANDS

POLYNESIA

• CHRISTMAS ISLAND   EQUATOR   0°

MARQUESAS
ISLANDS

SAMOA ISLANDS

BORA BORA

COOK
ISLANDS   TUAMOTU ARCHIPELAGO

TROPIC OF CAPRICORN 23°27'

PITCAIRN
ISLAND   EASTER
                                 ISLAND

SOUTH PACIFIC

OCEANIA

The sea furnishes a large part of the Micronesian food. In addition to all sorts of fish, they eat shrimp, crabs, sea slugs, octopus, and sea worms. The scarce sea turtle is considered a special delicacy.

Taro and breadfruit are among the more common plant foods. The natives soak the breadfruit in sea water, peel it, and then mash it to a pulp. Finally, they knead, roll and bake it, much as bread is prepared in Western lands. Breadfruit trees were the cargo which Captain Bligh, of H.M.S. *Bounty*, was transporting to the West Indies when his crew mutinied. This famous mutiny is described in the book *Mutiny on the Bounty* by Charles Nordhoff and James Norman Hall.

Clothing is only a slight problem to the inhabitants of

Fishing among Fiji islanders is a community affair. These natives have formed a large circle on an outer reef to trap fish in a large pocket net.

Fiji Official

The sea is an ever-present element in the lives of the natives of Oceania.

Air France

A native of Tahiti skillfully tossing his fishing net into a quiet lagoon.

the balmy climate of Micronesia. Sometimes brightly colored wrap-around cloth suffices for both men and women. The men may wear khaki shorts, the women Mother Hubbards, a nightgown-like garment that was brought to the islands by the missionaries in the nineteenth century.

At one time natives made their own cloth, using the fine

inner bark of the breadfruit tree. It was soaked in salt water until the fibers were loosened. Then it was pounded with wooden clubs into thin flat sheets. The material, called tapa cloth, was finally decorated with colorful patterns.

Laundering in Oceania.

Children of Oceania.

The homes of many Micronesians are simple structures; a framework of coconut logs is covered with a thatched roof. The roofs, made principally of palm leaves, are sometimes better able to withstand typhoons than those on the white man's houses. The walls are mats woven from pandanus leaves or coconut fronds. When guests come, the mats are taken down and spread on the floor for sitting.

While on a trip through the forests of Tahiti, Darwin was impressed by the way natives built him a snug shelter using only what was at hand. He wrote in his journal, "By the aid of strips of bark for rope, and the stems of bamboo for rafters, and the large leaf of the banana for a thatch,

For the first time in the history of Tonga, safe piped water was made available in villages, with W.H.O. assistance.

World Health Organization

A policeman in Suva.
Matson Lines

Tahitians in a few minutes built us an excellent house; and with withered leaves made a soft bed."

Less advanced culturally are the natives of Melanesia, particularly those on the islands of New Guinea and New Britain. Bushy-haired, stockily built and with blue-black skin, these people follow a way of life that is closer to the Stone Age than the present. However, as they come into contact with modern civilization they are slowly changing their living habits.

Once they were fierce warriors who practiced head-hunting and cannibalism. Despite strict controls, authorities on New Guinea and New Britain are not sure that these customs have been stamped out. They report, though, that the natives have abandoned their ancient practice of slaying widows so dead husbands might have company in the other world; killing one of a new-born pair of twins; "pointing of the bone," a ritual of magic intended to cause a victim's death.

The Australian aborigines are unique among the unusual racial groups in Oceania. They were the original settlers of Australia and are believed to have arrived when that continent and Asia were no more than a stone's throw apart. Only a shallow, narrow sea may have separated the two land masses, permitting the aborigines to wade across. Now they are largely confined to the hot, desert areas of northern Australia. They wear no clothes and live wholly outdoors. They do not build shelters, but are nomadic, hunting and gathering their food wherever they find it.

The aborigines are not particular when it comes to food. Their diet includes kangaroos which, more often than not, they do not bother to cook, emus, snakes, turtles, crocodiles, ants, and worms. They gather wild fruits, nuts, and honey, when in season. These aloof, strange people rely on nature's bounty for their survival, which in this barren part of the tropical world is none too plentiful.

Food gathering is a full-time occupation and one in which the whole family participates. The men, with their faithful hunting dogs, called dingos, go after the bigger game, such as kangaroos. Their only weapon is a wooden spear, hurled with great speed and accuracy. The women may pick berries and fruit, while children often dig in the soil for ants and worms.

Since his homeland is largely desert, water is a special problem for the aborigine. He has learned to overcome this difficulty in several ways. The easiest is by following rain squalls and drinking from the resulting puddles. During the dry season, he looks for water holes, scoops out the wet sand, and sucks it. Certain trees and shrubs that store water in their roots are dug out of the ground and sucked. Finally, when really desperate for water, the aborigine will search for a froglike creature that during the rainy season puffs up its body to almost twice its size with excess water, storing it for a dry period. When an aborigine comes upon one of these mobile water tanks, he feels lucky indeed.

Aborigine musicians. One man is a drummer, clicking sticks rhythmically. The other blows a didjeridoo, *a drone pipe made of a hollowed-out tree limb.*

Australian News Information Bureau

The Australian aborigines, who once numbered 300,000, are fast disappearing. More and more are giving up their nomadic life for town and city living or are taking jobs on the big sheep ranches of Australia.

The inhabitants of Central and South America, though not as diverse as the peoples of southeast tropical Asia, Indonesia and Oceania, are equally interesting. The range of their cultural levels is similar and in ancient times they had amazingly progressive civilizations—the Aztec and Mayan in Central America, and the Inca in South America.

Long before the first European explorers set foot on the soil of the American tropics, the Indians were supreme. Known variously as Aztecs, Mayans, and Incas, they had developed a cultural life that, in some respects, was comparable to that of ancient Egypt and Greece. Examples of their artistic and engineering skills still exist in the ruins of temples, public buildings and roadways in the forests of Mexico and high on the Andes Mountains.

After the Spanish conquest and the arrival of the Europeans who followed, the Indian civilizations disappeared. In their place over the course of many years there evolved new peoples and new cultures. Together with pure-blooded Indians, formerly the sole inhabitants of the American tropics, there are now European whites, mestizos (a mixture of European and non-Caucasian stock such as Indian), and Negroes.

The Indians often are the most backward of tropical America's inhabitants. They have progressed little since the days of the Spanish conquistadores. The majority live in small towns and villages tucked away in the folds of mountains stretching from Mexico to Paraguay. They are almost com-

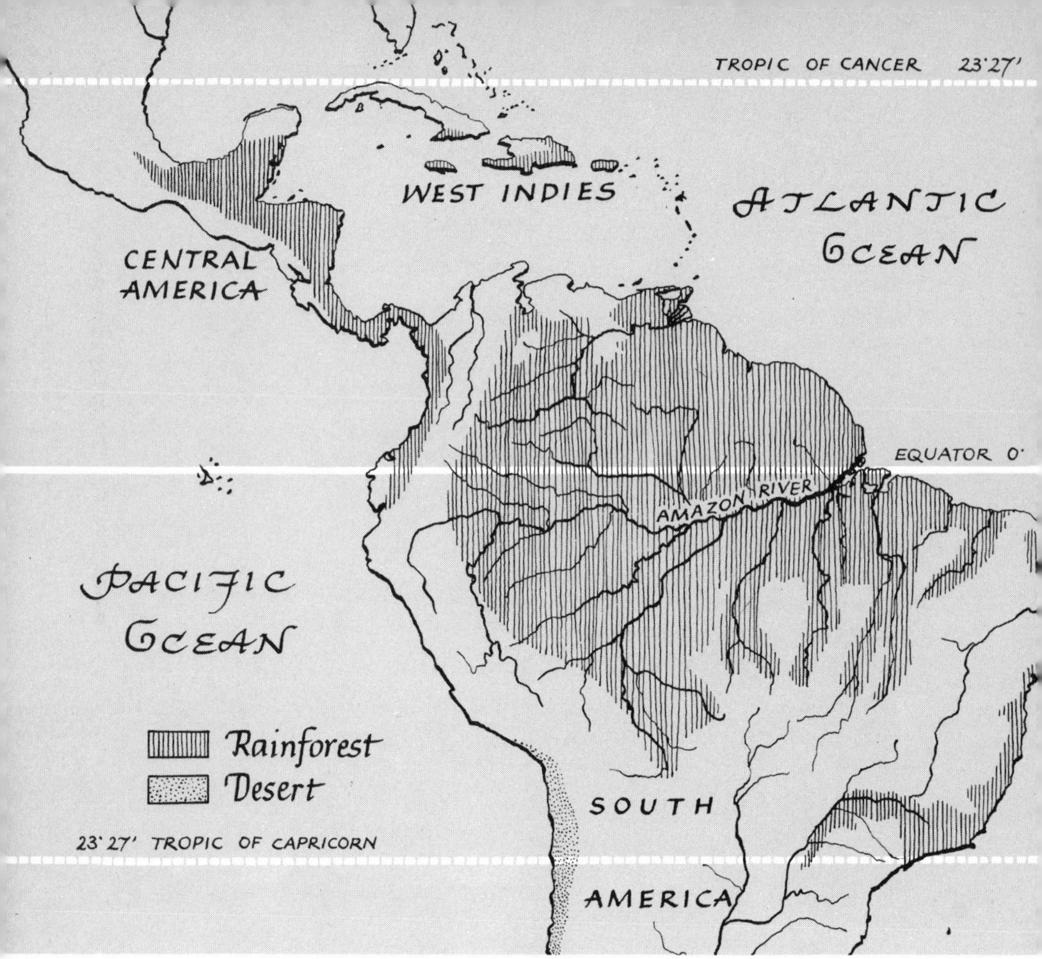

WEST INDIES

CENTRAL
AMERICA

ATLANTIC
OCEAN

EQUATOR 0˚

AMAZON RIVER

PACIFIC
OCEAN

||||| Rainforest
▒▒▒ Desert

23˚ 27' TROPIC OF CAPRICORN

SOUTH

AMERICA

pletely shut off from the outside world. Indians obtain their
livelihood mainly from agriculture.

White Europeans usually are the most advanced culturally.
Their ancestors brought from Europe a highly developed way
of life. In time they acquired control of the lands they had
settled, developed an agriculture and exploited the region's
mineral resources. The European culture became concentrated in large cities where today there are fine universities,
magnificent cathedrals, opera houses, symphony halls and

examples of the most modern forms of twentieth-century architecture. Europeans have helped develop efficient highway and communication systems. They have become presidents, cabinet members, governors and mayors in many governments.

The mestizos make up the majority in the population of such countries as Mexico, El Salvador, Honduras, Colombia, and Venezuela. Some mestizos have risen to positions of high authority and prestige in the government, military services, industry, and education. This is particularly true in those countries where the mestizos dominate the population, as in Mexico and Venezuela.

Teaching school children about the different foods and their nutritional value.

World Health Organization
(Paul Almasy)

The majority of the mestizos are peasants who farm the land for a livelihood. It is among these that their Indian heritage tends to become more evident, especially in the practice of religion. Most are members of the Roman Catholic faith, first brought to tropical America by the Spanish. But in accepting the beliefs of this religion some mestizos have not given up completely the primitive Indian form of worship. For example, witchcraft is still evoked to cure sickness.

The language of the mestizos also reflects their dual background. While Spanish is spoken throughout tropical America, many Indian words are also used: tortilla, tamale, and maize are well-known examples.

In the Amazon River Basin of Brazil live another people of mixed heritage. The Caboclos are part Indian, Portuguese, and Negro. Their language is Portuguese, liberally sprinkled with Indian. It is so different from the Portuguese spoken in the rest of Brazil that it is said a man needs a dictionary to understand it.

The original Indian culture has also left its imprint on the food and drink consumed by the Caboclos. They depend for nourishment mainly on corn, beans, peppers, peanuts, and manioc, all long familiar to the Indian. Manioc, a starchy root plant, is their most important staple, as it is with other tropical peoples. It is baked and eaten in place of bread, used as an ingredient in other dishes, and made into a drink called "Chihe."

Like the mestizo, the Caboclos' religion is a combination of Roman Catholicism and primitive supernatural beliefs.

Opposite: *A barrel maker in Colombia.*

World Health Organization
(Paul Almasy)

The cultural pattern of the peoples of tropical Central and South America has been influenced almost as much by the Negro as by the white man. Negroes were brought from Africa not long after the coming of the first white settlers, to serve as slaves, mainly on cotton and sugar plantations. They played a particularly important role in the cultural life of certain areas of Brazil, which had more slaves in the seventeenth and eighteenth centuries than any other portion of the New World and the Caribbean Islands.

In the West Indies, the original inhabitants, the Carib Indians, were almost completely annihilated within a period of fifty years after the arrival of the white man. Negroes were brought to the islands to take their place on the sugar plantations. Eventually, they became the principal racial group throughout the West Indies. As a result, many aspects of life—language, food, music, and dancing—have felt the imprint of the Negro's African heritage.

The popular samba from Brazil is basically Negro in origin. During the period of plantation life, on holidays, slaves danced to its rhythm around blazing fires. Many Brazilian folk tales can trace their origin to the world of Africa. One such story tells about a frightening character, "Quibung," who was half human and half animal, and swallowed bad children through a hole in his back.

The most primitive of the peoples of tropical Central and South America are isolated Indian tribes living deep in the interior of the Amazon rain forests. They are primarily hunters and food gatherers. Generally hostile toward outsiders, they usually are armed with bamboo spears, bows and arrows, blow guns that shoot poison-tipped darts, and machetes. Strange, barbaric rituals are an important part of their cultural life.

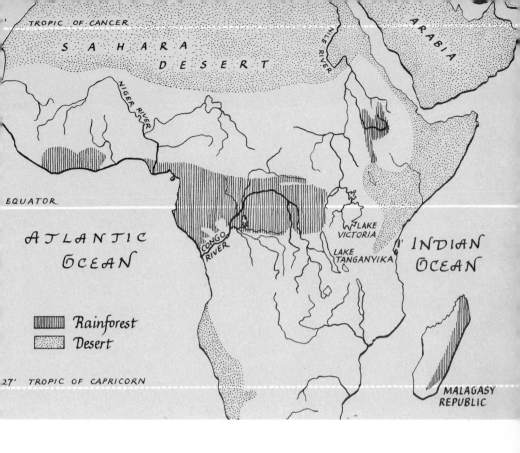

Tropical Africa, more than twice as large as the United States, has, according to ethnologists, ten basic racial groups. But if other than ethnological standards are used, such as variations in language, historical, and cultural background, then it has more than seven hundred kinds of people.

Africa has long been considered the traditional home of the black man. But there are many inhabitants of other skin colorings who also consider themselves true Africans. The main tropical native African groups are the Pygmy-Bushmen, Negro, Hamite, and Semite.

The Pygmy is the smallest human being in the world. He averages 54 inches in height. Brown skinned and beau-

*Arab merchant display-
ing his vegetables at an
open-air market.*

tifully formed, he is a forest dweller who obtains his food
by hunting, digging up edible wild plants, or plucking fruit
from trees. He is considered one of the best hunters in Africa.
Even the biggest game, elephants and rhinoceroses, fall victim to this fearless little giant. Most pygmies today live in
the rain forests of the Republic of Congo, the Quesso region
of the Congo Republic, the Gabon Republic, the Cameroons,
and Angola.

This proud African is reluctant to give up the old ways.

Below: *Tropical Africans also have traffic jams.*

The true Negro and his two principal offshoots, the Nilotic and Bantu Negro, form the largest group in tropical Africa's population. They number about 125 million.

The true Negro is of average build with skin color ranging from dark brown to black. Most have hair that is black and kinky, thick lips, and a broad, flat nose. About sixty million true Negroes live in the rain and dry forest belts of West Africa, from the Senegal River eastward to the Cameroons. Some of the rain tribes include the Kru from Liberia, Fanti from Ghana, and the Yoruba of Nigeria. Many of the slaves brought to America two and a half centuries ago came from these tribes.

The Hamite is an African of ancient Caucasian background. Although his skin is light brown, his thin nose, narrow face, and thin lips are Caucasian. Hamites live in Ethiopia and Eritrea. In Ethiopia (once known as Abyssinia) they inhabit one of the oldest kingdoms on earth. Legend has it that the kingdom was started several thousand years ago when King Solomon fathered a child by the Queen of Sheba, who came from Ethiopia. Their son, brought back to the land of his mother, became King Menelik I. He is considered the founder of the royal dynasty currently ruling Ethiopia. The present ruler, Haile Selassie, is said to be the 225th in line from King Menelik I. Emperor Selassie is known to his people by various titles: Elect of God, Conquering Lion of Judah, King of Zion, and King of Kings.

One interesting group of Africans which does not seem to fit into any of the four groups are the Hottentots who live in South Africa. Some feel they were separated from the Caucasians in prehistoric time; others feel that due to similarities in language they are the lost Hamites. But the Hamite theory is disputed by many because the Hottentot language is also similar to that of the Bushmen. Clicks are often used at the beginnings of words by both the Bushmen and Hottentots. The yellow skin of the Hottentots has been an enigma to anthropologists who want to fit all people into groups. There is little agreement on a classification system for Africans. The Hottentots are an example as to why there is such a lack of agreement.

A number of factors distinguish Africa's different racial groups. Living habits are one of the more important. Tropical Africans who have not adopted Western standards are loosely lumped into four main groups—hunters, food gatherers, herdsmen, and farmers.

A family of nomads from Somalia with all their possessions.
World Health Organization (Eric Schwab)

Hunters, such as the Bushmen and Pygmies, are nomads who live in temporary shelters made of wood, grass, and reeds worked into the shape of a beehive. Their hunting weapons are the simplest: a wooden bow, spears, and throwing stick. Bowstrings are made from animal sinews; arrows from reeds and bone. Flint stone and iron scraping tools are used to shape wood and clean animal hides. The skins of animals are made into bags for carrying liquids and foods and into clothing.

Food gatherers are on about the same cultural level as the Bushmen and Pygmies. Wild fruits and edible plants are their main food supplies. Typical are the Babinga people,

A Somalia native woman grinding maize on a stone slab.

World Health Organization (Eric Schwab)

who build crude rectangular huts, made with sticks, leaves, and lianas, a tropical climbing plant. The interior usually has a bed constructed of bark and leaves. Since food gatherers are also nomadic, new shelters are built wherever food supplies are found. In their hot and humid land, these Africans have little use for clothing. The men wear a loin cloth made of bark and the women a covering of leaves.

Food gatherers have fewer tools than the hunters. The two most important are a "tinderbox" made of a hard and a soft wood which, when rubbed together, produce a flame, and an iron spear for hunting. Occasionally they vary their fruit and plant diet with meat.

Somalia nomad women building an "akhal" or hut.
World Health Organization (Eric Schwab)

African herdsmen are a step higher on the cultural ladder. Because they do not wander in search of food, their homes are more elaborate. They are generally made of long strips of pliable wood, firmly held together with ropes of osier and then covered with animal hides. Sometimes the walls and roofs are covered with grass and then plastered with a mixture of fresh dung and mud. Beds made of poles or piles of straw over which animal hides are placed, a stool or two, and gourds for holding milk and water complete the furnishings.

Herdsmen include the Masai, the Tusi, Suk, and the Fulani. Many look upon their cattle as a symbol of prestige rather than as an economic asset. The number of cows and bulls a man has often indicates his wealth and standing in a tribe. He seldom sells his cattle or slaughters them for food. They are eaten only if they die a natural death. Occasionally one may be sacrificed at a wedding, or initiation ceremony for a boy entering manhood, or at a funeral.

The herds provide milk, curds, cheese and butter. The Masai, once fierce warriors, are particularly fond of blood drawn from the necks of bulls and cows and drunk plain or mixed with milk. Years ago when there were frequent battles between tribes, the Masai gorged themselves on cattle blood and meat for several days before going into combat. This diet was supposed to give them greater strength and stamina.

The farmers' huts are similar to the herdsmens'. Sometimes they have two rooms instead of one. In addition to a bed of straw or animal hides and a homemade blanket, there may be a pestle and mortar (for mashing vegetables and fruit), pots for holding water and for cooking foods, digging sticks and hoes for farming, and a carving knife.

Nearly all tropical Africans belong to closely knit tribes. A common language and a similar cultural background hold them together. Within the tribes are still smaller units called clans, where blood relationships may extend from the mother's or father's side to many distant family connections. Tribalism is far more of a unifying force among these people than the nationalism now sweeping parts of Africa.

A particular tribe of natives will scar their cheeks, make bumps on their bodies by rubbing ashes into open cuts, file their teeth to points, wear large discs in their lower lips, or distend their ear lobes into looping strings. Under the influences of the twentieth century, however, these customs are fading. It has been asserted that such curious customs were begun to discourage slave hunters. The hunters would not take disfigured natives.

An African tribal chief being installed into office.
Twentieth Century Fund

A tribe may consist of a few small families or hundreds of large ones. One country may then have many tribes. In Ghana, for example, there are about 100 tribes, each with its own chief. Whatever their number, tribes are unified by a chief who is the supreme ruler. He has the power of life or death over his subjects and, as a result, is held in the highest respect.

African chief in tribal dress.

Firestone News Service

In these tribes which follow the old ways many unusual tribal customs exist between a chief and his people. In some tribes it is forbidden for anyone to look at the chief if he eats in public. Others make it a serious crime for women to look upon their chief. In still other tribes, the chief's spittle is never permitted to fall upon the ground for fear some evil spirit will take it and use the kingly power to bring harm to the monarch's people. Servants follow their ruler around with spittoons.

Some chiefs are elected to their position, while others inherit the throne. But as with other traditional African ways, the authority of tribal chiefs is weakening under the impact of change. Councils of young, educated men are taking over control of tribal affairs. Kings, as elsewhere in the world, are becoming figureheads.

More than five hundred different tongues are spoken by tropical Africans. In some extreme instances, the language differences are so great that neighboring tribes on opposite river banks find it almost impossible to communicate with one another.

One of the more widespread and better-known African languages is Ki-Swahili. This is the common speech of most East Africans and the chief language in the Bantu family of languages, of which there are 183. Swahili has been called the worthiest and most dignified of all African Negro tongues, mainly because of its literary quality. A dozen newspapers are printed in the Swahili tongue, as well as books of poetry and even translations from European literature. Some Swahili words have found their way into the English language, *bwana,* meaning "master," for example, and *safari,* meaning "journey."

Hausa is another important language, used by millions of

inhabitants living in the western part of Africa. Hausa has two written forms, Arabic and English. Arab and Christian missionaries developed the written form of Hausa so the natives of Africa could read their respective religious books —the Koran and the Bible.

Tropical Africans have been reluctant to abandon completely their native religious beliefs for those of the Western world. Islam was brought into the dark continent by Arab traders and slave dealers, Christianity by Europeans. Wherever the new religions took root, the natives adapted them to their own long-held beliefs.

The native religion of the primitive African is complex and consists of numerous deities and rites of magic. Each of the deities is surrounded by its own lore, has its special priesthood and rituals, and its individual group of worshipers. Rituals are often elaborate and usually take place as part of a yearly festival which may last a week or longer. Sometimes the religious part of a festival is held in secret with only the high priest and his aids participating. The public portions are colorful and frequently involve thousands of people.

African deities are called upon to answer requests of husbands and wives for children and of farmers for a good crop, to bring good luck and wealth. They also have the power to punish wrongdoers, especially those who mistreat their fellow tribesman.

Magic is an important element in African religion and is based on the power of charms and medicines. Every tribe has its witch doctor who dispenses this magic. Hollow gourds holding magic medicines and beans are symbols of his trade. Witch doctors wield a strong influence, but their services are used mostly to cure illness.

Artistic creativeness plays a significant part in the life of

primitive Africans. The telling of folk tales, the making of
colorful masks, wood carving, decorative bead and basket
work are popular. But the artistic forms in which most
Africans seem to find their greatest expression are music and
dancing. It has been said that for Africans, dancing is as
natural as walking and children dance as soon as they learn
to walk.

Drums are the most important musical instrument and
beat out lively rhythms for the dances. They also serve the
practical purpose of communication. Africans living as far as

*Like happy school children the world over, these African youngsters dash
madly for home after dismissal from classes.*

Ivory Coast Service of Information

Above: *Students are assembling at a Belgian Catholic missionary school in the Congo.*

Opposite page, top: *An African student sculptor working on his piece which he has called "Slaves."*

Opposite: *Many Africans are giving up the old tribal ways for life in cities. These women are working in a Nigeria canning company.*

a mile apart will often send messages to one another via a "drum" language.

In this modern age Africans are experiencing radical changes in their lives. Just as peoples in other areas of the tropical world, they are gaining control of their own lands. New nations, such as the republics of Ghana, Senegal, and Nigeria, have come into existence to take their proud place beside the older established countries of the world. And great numbers of the people are giving up the ways of the bush country for a life in cities and towns.

Typical examples of African native art.

Despite the adoption of modern ways, many Africans still like to perform their tribal dances.

4

TROPICAL PLANTS
AND ANIMALS

SCIENTISTS ESTIMATE that almost 75 per cent of the known plant specimens in the world can be found in the tropics. Each of the region's climate zones produces its own distinct plant life.

In the rain forests of the equatorial climate, where the temperature is high throughout the year and the rainfall heavy and frequent, grow the lushest and most exotic of tropical plants. Even poles supporting electric power lines have been known to sprout leaves under these hothouse conditions. The trees may grow as high as 130 feet, their crowns creating a thick umbrella of leaves that effectively shuts out much of the light and hot sun. The trunks of the trees are amazingly straight; the first branches begin about 70 to 100 feet above the ground. Because they struggle with one another to reach sunlight, the trees do not bear many branches. Only a diffused light, shot through by beams of sunshine, illumines the forests.

Hours after a tropical downpour, the leafy canopy above continues to shower drops of water. During periods when there is no rain, the tree tops sprinkle sap or resin on the ground below. Thus there seems to be a constant dripping within the shadowy realm of the rain forest.

The rain forest floor is covered with rotted tree trunks, shrubby plant life, and tree roots. The roots lie largely on the surface soaking up moisture. They wind and twist over wide areas. Together with dense bushes and lianas they make hiking through a rain forest frequently difficult. Experienced travelers say that in these places even with a machete to cut the vines and bushes, they can cover only about five miles in a day's march. Rain forests do have clear areas. Where the foliage is so dense that no light penetrates, plant life cannot survive and the ground beneath the trees is open.

The green world of the rain forests is broken only occasionally by the flamboyant colors of blossoming trees and vines. The American jacaranda exhibits huge patches of brilliant violet. The tulip tree is a vibrant scarlet. The bright blossoms of flowering vines push up through the leafy barrier of the tree tops, providing startling spots of color. But these are exceptions in a sea of uniform green.

Many tropical plants have unusual forms and odd-shaped fruit. A unique example is the sausage-tree. Its fruit looks just like the bolognas one sees hanging in the butcher shop window.

Some tropical plants scatter their ripened seeds with a loud "popping" sound. The sand-box tree is one of these.

If there is a single plant that can be said to be truly typical of the rain forest, it is the liana. Its vines lace the forests like ropes, some as thick as a man's body and stretching to enormous lengths. They may be round as a steel cable or flat as ribbon. Some have bumps, as though they were knotted. All provide a big obstacle to travelers.

As they grow, lianas support themselves on trees or other lianas. They wind around tree trunks or hang on with sucker roots, hooks, and tendrils. Once they reach the roof of the forest, they begin to sprout branches. Then they bend down toward the earth again. Back on solid ground, the vines continue to grow in twists, loops, and great, complicated entanglements.

Many tropical lianas have considerable value. Rattan is obtained from one kind, a material used to make baskets. This liana is the longest species, often reaching a length of more than six hundred feet in the forests of Malaya, Sumatra, and Borneo.

The young leaves of a species of liana which grows in the rain forests of Ecuador supply a supple fiber from which Panama hats are made. In the Amazon basin there are lianas that produce a fruit from which Brazilians make one of their national drinks—guarana. The Passion-flower and its edible fruit is still another of the useful lianas. The flower is so named because its form supposedly resembles some of the instruments used in Christ's crucifixion. From others come rubber latex and ingredients for medicines. Forest dwellers used the powdered particles of some lianas as a drug to stupefy and catch river fish.

Throughout the rain forests are plants that depend on other plants for their existence. Often these are lumped together into one family and called parasitic plants. Actually, however, naturalists have found that there are two distinct groups—epiphytes and parasites. Epiphytes merely use other plants for support, they do not feed on the host plant. Lianas are a good example of these. Others are ferns, mosses, and orchids. Epiphytes obtain the greater part of the moisture they need from the atmosphere. As a result, they are confined mainly to the wettest areas of the tropical rain forests.

Nature has given epiphyte plants interesting characteristics to enable them to live far from the soil. Some have very thick leaves for storing water; others have leaves that are arranged for catching rain water and falling debris from tree tops; still others, such as orchids, have long, dangling aerial roots, both for anchoring the plant to a host and for obtaining nourishment.

Parasitic plants are less common. They obtain all sustenance from the plants on which they grow. One of the more unusual of these specimens is the rafflesia of Sumatra. The seeds of this plant are carried by birds or by the wind until finally they lodge in the crevices of the bark of a tree. Once comfortably in place, the seeds sprout, getting their nourishment from the sap of the tree. In time the seed develops into a plant, producing an enormous dark purple flower. The blossom gives off an odor that is attractive to flies which pollinate the plant.

Tropical orchid.
U. S. Department of Agriculture

Perhaps the best known of the plants outside the rain forest is the palm tree. It comes from a large family numbering more than a thousand species. Palm trees grow throughout the tropics, but are particularly at home in southeast Asia, Indonesia, and the Amazon River region. Some palms are the most useful of all tropical flora. More than one primitive civilization has depended on the palm tree for its survival. A particularly valuable member of the group is the coconut palm.

This tree is believed to have originated in Indonesia. It is found mostly along the seacoast, and the sea has been the principal means by which it has spread throughout the tropics. Since the nuts are buoyant and unharmed by salt water, ocean currents carry them great distances until they bump ashore on some distant land and take root. Wherever a coral reef has been newly created or a volcanic island born, the coconut palms are among the first plants to appear.

Man has also been an important factor in the palm tree's migrations, planting it for personal and commercial use throughout the tropics.

Inhabitants of the tropics have long depended on the coconut palm for three essentials of life—food, clothing and shelter. The inner white flesh and colorless liquid of the coconuts provide food and drink. It takes five years for a tree to reach maturity and produce nuts. To reach the nuts, natives scamper with great agility up tree trunks, which often grow sixty feet high.

The leaves and trunk of the coconut palm supply materials for shelter and clothing. The tree trunks are usually

Opposite: *The talipot palm.*
U. S. Department of Agriculture

employed to build the frameworks of the houses, the leaves and branches for the roofs and sides. Fibers are stripped from leaves and woven into clothing.

The value of the coconut palm has spread far beyond the borders of the tropics. Oil from the dried meat of the nut, called copra, is used by a number of industries in the northern latitudes. It is particularly prized by soap manufacturers, some of whom consume it in such large quantities that they maintain their own coconut palm groves. Makers of oleomargarine and nitroglycerine also find the oil important for their products.

The peach palm, a common fruit tree of tropical America. Fruits are yellow, orange and red and hang in clusters.

U. S. Department of Agriculture

There are other palms almost as valuable as the coconut: the oil palm, found mostly in West Africa, whose oil is also used in the making of soap; the babassu palm of Brazil, the nuts of which yield an important industrial oil; the wax palm, whose leaves make an excellent wax. The seeds of the wax palm are also boiled by the natives as a substitute for coffee.

Sugar palms yield a sap from which sugar is made. When fermented, the sap produces a sparkling drink called palm wine.

The sago palm is another food source. A thick, starch-like substance imbedded in its fat stems is dug out by natives, washed thoroughly and eaten. Palm cabbage is also a popular food. The terminal bud of any species of palm forms an edible food. It looks like a big chunk of ivory and has a nut-like taste.

The Theban palm that thrives in the dry areas of tropical Africa is valued for its leaves, which furnish fibers for textiles. A similar species is the raphia palm from which raffia is obtained and used for making baskets and hats.

The mangrove is one of the numerous aquatic plants that inhabit large areas of the tropics. It thrives in the brackish water of swampland and forms a dense belt along a number of tropical coastlines. It is also found around stagnant lagoons and in the estuaries of rivers. In some areas mangrove swamps stretch sixty miles inland from the coast. The largest swamps are in Africa, Malagasy, Indonesia, Central and South America, and the islands of Oceania.

Mangroves grow about fifty feet high. Their root systems form a spidery, impenetrable complex mass. Part of this consists of aerial roots that grow downward from the branches. The ground-level roots are often covered by the sea during high tide. When the waters recede, the roots, coated with

slimy mud, are exposed. All sorts of marine life—oysters, crabs, and fish—cling to them. During World War II mangroves were familiar obstacles to American soldiers making amphibious landings on the islands of the southwest Pacific.

Mangrove swamps have some value. Mud deposits around the roots and solidifies, especially at the mouths of rivers, and in this way, coastal land is built up. Also an acid is obtained from the bark of mangrove trees and employed for tanning leather.

More delicate aquatic plants are the lotus and water lily. The lotus is found chiefly in southeast Asia. Its leaves, shaped like cups, stand high above the surface of the water, while those of the water lily float on the surface.

The water lily grows best in the Amazon region. One of the most unusual water lilies is the *Victoria regia,* which flourishes in the swamps bordering the Amazon river. It has large, flat leaves with turned up edges and is six feet in diameter when full grown. A mammoth specimen once measured eight feet, six inches. Strong and buoyant, they can support sixty-five pounds without sinking. Their flowers are proportionally large, and grow up to sixteen inches wide. When they appear in December and January they are purple with a white border. Later, the fragrant blossoms change to pink, opening in the evening and closing with the approach of morning. After the flower dies, a ball-like pod, filled with edible, starchy seeds, is formed.

These are only a few of the botanical specimens that flourish in the torrid zone. There are many others that are of economic value to the inhabitants of the tropics and to the

Opposite: *Grove of giant bamboo trees.*
U. S. Department of Agriculture

Loading bananas.

rest of the world as well: the spice plants—cinnamon, nut-meg, clove and pepper; and, of course, bananas, coffee, tea, rice, and rubber.

The animal life of no other region on earth can match that of the tropics in numbers, variety of species, sizes, shapes, and colors. The largest populations of most of the world's biggest mammals, the elephant, rhinoceros, and hippopota-mus, are concentrated here. Infinite numbers of insects also make their home in the tropics. Indeed, although science has classified many thousands of them, thousands more are still to be catalogued. It is among insects, too, that the tropics truly excel in respect to variety of species. As an example, in the Panama Canal Zone on a tiny island in Gatun Lake there is a nature reserve called Barro Colorado. On this small portion of the tropics, about six square miles in extent, scientists have identified some 20,000 species of insects.

Bigness is a remarkable characteristic among tropical animals. The huge bulk of the elephant and hippopotamus of the mammals is a familiar representative. Huge size is also a feature of the insect world. The biggest butterflies, moths, and beetles, among others, are found in the torrid zone. Some species of moth have a wing span of a foot. Beetles measuring three inches from nose to tail are common. Some trap-door spiders grow to the size of a small plate.

The hornbill is an easy bird to train.
Kantoor Voor, Dutch East Indies

The varied shapes of tropical animals are another of their distinguishing features. The long-necked giraffe, the square-ness of the elephant with its supple trunk, and the squat, barrel-shaped body of the hippopotamus are distinct and well known. If we move again to the opposite scale of the animal world, to the insect, odd shapes are even more common and remarkable. Endless examples could be cited such as that of some membracids, tree-hopping bugs with weird upward twisting bodies. Shape, as well as color, is nature's way of helping tropical animals survive in their environment.

Nature has been particularly lavish in dispensing colors

The white cockatoo is found throughout Australia, the Molucca Islands, and New Guinea. He is no friend of the farmer, since the cockatoo loves to eat crops.

Australian News and
Information Bureau

to the animals of the tropics. With some creatures, color rather than form is their outstanding feature. This is especially true among birds, a number of which wear the most brilliant plumage in the world.

Pittas (birds confined mainly to the area of southeast Asia and Australia), parakeets, and birds of paradise flashing myriad shades of red, yellow, green and blue, often in striking patterns, are a few outstanding specimens. Frogs that dwell in tree tops and lizards present equally dazzling colors.

But not all creatures in the tropics are brightly colored. Nature has given a number of them more subdued hues which blend with the background of the forest, clever camouflage against predatory enemies.

Besides their interesting physical characteristics, tropical fauna are also remarkable for their unusual habitats. One large group, known as tree dwellers, rarely, if ever, comes down to the ground. Another equally numerous band lives only on the surface. Then there is a big population that likes to divide its wanderings between the open spaces above ground and the dark, subterranean levels. Finally, there are others that move freely back and forth between the three worlds.

The tree-top population is believed to be the biggest of all. Among the more familiar life in this lofty world of leaves are the birds—the different kinds of parakeets, toucans, hornbills, and birds of paradise. Most of them feed on leaves and fruit. Some are birds of prey and prefer meat, as does the Harpy eagle, with its sharp, powerful beak and claws and distinctive crest. This bird lives in the tropical forests of South and Central America and the Philippines. The American Harpy hunts the sloth for food, while his Philippine cousin prefers to stalk monkeys.

Monkeys and apes inhabit the tree tops. The capuchin monkey, the howler, and the spider monkey are all indigenous to tropical America. Elsewhere in the tropics the gibbon and chimpanzee are common. The chimpanzee spends some of its time on the ground. Its favorite foods are nuts, fruits, and tender green shoots, though some prefer young birds, eggs, and insects. Tree-top monkey dwellers usually travel in packs, swinging from branch to branch, their loud chatter echoing through the forest. When the day's wanderings are over, chimpanzees build nests of leaves in the highest parts of the trees. Safe and secure in their lofty perches, they then proceed to sing one another to sleep with monkey lullabies.

One of the more unusual of the tree inhabitants is the sloth. This creature makes its home up in the trees of the rain forest. It hangs upside down from tree limbs by its long, sharp claws.

Squirrels, mice, chameleons, iguanas, forest geckos, boa constrictors, and pythons are other tree-top dwellers along with the monkeys and sloths. In the trees, too, are countless varieties of insects including the most colorful butterflies in the world, grasshoppers, crickets, mantids, and, surprisingly enough, ants. Many ants prefer the trees to the ground. Some build nests of leaves, using their larvae to bind the leaves together. Others construct tiny nests on the undersides of leaves, with bits of earth and twigs.

Ants also live on the earth's surface, the second great domain of tropical fauna. Here they keep company with lions, tigers, giraffes, rhinoceroses, elephants and hippos. An outstanding group of surface-living ants is the voracious leaf-cutters. Fantastically busy workers, they can completely strip a tree of its leaves in a single day. The leaves are chewed into microscopic pieces which are then carried to underground nests to form gardens for growing fungi.

Other ants are more warlike and prefer meat to leaves. Armies of these little creatures sally out on morning raids and gobble up great quantities of insects. A favorite prey of some are termites, a close relative of ants.

Termites live both above and below ground. They are spectacular builders of above-ground nests. These are often taller than a man and are made of clay, which the termites bring from underground, and chewed-up bits of wood. Because of the termites' voracious appetites, a number of trees are no more than hollow shells. Although they may look sturdy, a single blow from an axe can topple them to the ground.

One of the strangest termite nests is found on Cape York peninsula in Australia. Six feet high with flat sides, it looks like a tombstone in a graveyard. All the nests face in the same direction, along one of the earth's magnetic lines of force. Because of this, the insects that build them are called "magnetic" termites. Scientists can only guess why these termites build their nests the way they do. A popular theory is that the nests point in the same direction to take the best possible advantage of the sun's rays, so the clay will harden quickly.

While ants and termites do a great deal of harm to plant life, they also accomplish much that is good. Their insatiable appetites lead them to consume a vast amount of forest debris—fallen trees, leaves, and vines—and convert it into valuable humus. The humus gives a springy feel to the floor of the tropical forest and helps to maintain its fertility.

Wandering through forest and field, wholly unaware of his termite neighbors, is the biggest of the tropical animals, the elephant. In prehistoric times, when great herds roamed over

The Asiatic elephant is often trained to do heavy hauling.

almost all of the earth, more than three hundred species of elephants existed. Now only two remain—the African and Asiatic elephants. The first is confined to tropical Africa and the second to India, Ceylon, Burma, Malaya, Indo-China, Sumatra, and Borneo.

The African elephant is the bigger of the two beasts. The bull will often weigh 7 tons and measure 11 feet high at the shoulders. Its ivory tusks may be 6 feet in length.

The Asiatic bull elephant averages six tons in weight and reaches a shoulder height of 8 feet. Its tusks are only 4 feet long.

The elephant has notoriously poor vision. It can barely see objects 100 feet away. But what it lacks in eyesight, it more than makes up for with an extraordinary sense of smell. The elephant's trunk is a mass of muscle and extremely flexible. The beast uses it with dexterity, lifting with equal ease a clump of grass or a ton of bricks.

Because of its great strength the elephant has been trained to haul logs and stack lumber in many forests of southeast Asia. In several countries, notably India, the elephant is often used in ceremonial parades. On these occasions the beast is decorated with richly colored trappings.

Another impressive giant is the giraffe, the tallest of tropical Africa's wild game. The giraffe may reach a height of 18 feet and weigh close to two tons. It is gentle by nature, but has great strength and, when aroused, defends itself with a powerful kick of its legs. Despite the giraffe's awkward size, it can gallop along at a speed of 30 miles an hour, moving with a peculiar rocking horse motion.

The treeless savanna is home to the giraffe. There it can better keep an eye open for its natural enemy, the lion. Like the elephant, the giraffe lives on a vegetable diet, mostly the

The long-necked giraffe has little trouble reaching his food, the leaves of trees.

leaves of trees. Before drinking, it spreads wide its forelegs and bends its long neck to the ground. When it returns to an upright position, it snaps its heels together like a soldier coming to attention.

In contrast to the restless giraffe, the squat, heavy hippopotamus prefers to 'snooze in the mud. Only the bull elephant is heavier than the hippo's three or four tons. Natives often refer to it as the river horse, because it spends its time wallowing in shallow river water and muddy swamps. The hippo's formidable size and tough hide protect it from enemies. Even natives leave it alone because, when angry, the hippo is dangerous and difficult to handle. Oddly enough, one of the

Rhinos love to wallow in swamps and munch on aquatic plants.

East Africa Tourist Travel Assn.

hippo's worst enemies is a tiny fly, which bites the soft flesh around its eyes. To get rid of the flies, the hippo plunges its head into the river or burrows deeper into the mud. It is probably because of this fly that the hippo spends so much of its time in rivers and swamps. When night falls, it waddles onto dry land in search of its supper—several hundred pounds of lush grass. The hippopotamus population is concentrated in tropical Africa between Lake Edward and Lake George in Rwanda and Burundi.

Tropical Africa also is the home of the traditional king of the jungle, the lion. The male sports a fur collar that makes it more distinctive than the female. The lion often has several mates who do the hard work of hunting and raising the cubs.

Two lions relaxing in the sun while a lioness watches from the shade.

South African Tourist Corp.

After the hunt for food is over, the female, who has stalked the prey, moves aside to let the male get his share of the "kill." Only when the king has his fill do the females step in to devour their portion. Last to eat are the cubs, who get the leftovers. The lion prefers to hunt and to live in the savanna lands, where the giraffe, among his favorite foods, can easily be had.

The rhinoceros is another member of Africa's big game population. This animal, almost as large and heavy as the hippo, is cantankerous by nature and will charge furiously at tormentors with its dangerous curved horn. Like elephants, rhinos have poor vision. But this handicap is compensated for by sharp hearing and a keen sense of smell.

The white rhino, a species fast disappearing from the African tropics.

South African Tourist Corp.

There are two species of rhinos, black and white. The white rhino is the less common and the larger of the two, weighing anywhere from two and a half to three tons. Hunters have killed most of the white rhinos in the African tropics. One of the biggest herds left lives within the protected confines of the Garamba National Park in the Congo. The black rhinos are much more numerous.

The creatures described in this chapter are only a handful of the great many that live in the tropical world. In Africa alone there are countless other animals: the impala, zebra, gnu, hyena, and wart-hog. Tropical America has its quota of which the cougar and anteater are representative. The

A trio of zebras.
South African Tourist Corp.

tiger of southeast Asia and the kangaroo of Australia and New Guinea may also be mentioned for the remainder of the tropics.

The tropics are veritably a gigantic zoo. Unhappily, the wild animals are being driven close to extinction. Changes throughout much of the tropics such as the construction of new villages and roads, the building of dams and the opening of new farming lands are destroying vital grazing areas and water holes. The animals are also being needlessly slaughtered by unscrupulous hunters. This is especially true of tropical Af-

Kangaroos are found in Australia, Tasmania, Papua and the Aru Islands. Their powerful hind legs enable them to bound as high as 25 feet and dash at speeds of more than 25 miles per hour.

Australian News and Information Bureau

A group of springbok in Kruger National Park.

Water bucks in Queen Elizabeth National Park, Uganda.

Zebra, eland, and wildebeest quenching their thirst at a waterhole.

rica's big game population. Elephants are being indiscriminately killed for their ivory tusks, which are said to be the basis of a million dollar business, an illegal business in the eyes of those seeking to protect Africa's precious animal life. The giraffe is another victim of senseless slaughter, simply because his tufted tail happens to make a good fly whisk.

Efforts are being made to put a halt to this destruction, mainly by the establishment of large game preserves. A good start has already been made with the creation of Serengeti

The gorilla population is rapidly dying out in the African tropics. A hunting party killed this giant specimen being held upright by a native.

Belgian Government Information Center

National Park in Tanganyika, Queen Elizabeth National Park in Uganda, Nairobi Royal National Park and Amboseli National Reserve, both in Kenya. Amboseli is one of the largest, spreading more than 1200 square miles over the African landscape at the foot of majestic Mount Kilimanjaro.

The vast variety of plant and animal life in the tropics also makes it an outdoor laboratory unequaled anywhere else on earth. To naturalists it is an endless, fascinating source of study. The national game parks will go a long way toward keeping the tropics that way, especially as more of them are established.

5

COPPER, COFFEE,
AND CINCHONA

THE FIRST of the riches which early European visitors to the tropics acquired were spices and silks. Later, with the discovery and conquest of tropical America, the list of treasures grew to include gold and silver. To Europeans of the sixteenth and seventeenth centuries the tropics were a region of undreamed-of wealth. What was true then is true today. Over the years as the tropics became better known, their storehouse of natural wealth proved truly astonishing. They have abundant and varied minerals, vast forests, and many different agricultural products.

Of all the areas, tropical Africa is among the wealthiest in natural resources. Indeed, few other regions in the world can match the array of its mineral riches alone. Uranium, copper, gold, diamonds, lead, tin, chromium, aluminum, iron, and zinc are all found there.

Immense deposits of uranium ore, a radioactive element and a source of atomic energy, exist in the Republic of Congo. In fact, geologists say that there is more radioactive mineral wealth in tropical Africa than any other place on earth.

Uranium ore was first discovered in the Republic of Congo in 1913. Two years later a rich vein was found near the village of Jadotville, which subsequently became one of the world's most important sources for radioactive minerals. It was from the uranium mines of the Republic of Congo that the fissionable material for the first atom bomb was obtained.

Copper has long been the most important mineral in tropical Africa's storehouse. It has been mined there on a large scale since 1910. There are several big copper deposits in Africa, but the largest and most important are in Northern Rhodesia and in the neighboring province of Katanga in the

Bulldozer at work in a copper mine in Katanga province of the Congo.

Belgian Government Information Center

Republic of Congo. These adjacent deposits form a copper belt over 250 miles long and 50 miles wide in some places. The combined area ranks as one of the world's largest producers of copper. Tropical Africa's vast copper reserves are estimated at one third of the world's total.

Nature has been equally generous with iron ore. Africa is believed to have sufficient deposits buried in its rugged terrain to last more than 100 years. The most valuable beds are in Northern Rhodesia, Southern Rhodesia, Uganda, and Liberia. In Liberia, one of the oldest of Africa's independent nations, the iron ore fields lie in the Bomi Hills, first prospected during World War II, when production of fighting equipment placed an enormous demand on the iron ore deposits in the United States. After encouraging reports from geologists, development of the fields was finally begun in the late 1940's. The first iron ore was shipped from the Bomi Hills in 1951. It went to the United States, which is still one of Liberia's best iron ore customers.

Other important mineral producing areas in the African tropics are the extensive bauxite deposits, a source of aluminum, in Ghana, the large fields of manganese in Ghana and in the Republic of Congo, the chromium beds in Southern Rhodesia, and cobalt in the Republic of Congo. The Congo is the world's largest producer of cobalt. Northern Rhodesia also has extensive cobalt deposits.

Gold, long the most highly prized of metals, is to be found at many places in tropical Africa. The three largest gold producing regions in tropical Africa are in Ghana, Southern Rhodesia, and the Republic of Congo. Ghana leads in the production, as it has since Portuguese explorers first discovered gold there five hundred years ago. Later it was found in such abundance that the region became known as the Gold Coast. The name remained until the Gold Coast became the independent state of Ghana in 1957. Today the most active gold mines are at the towns of Tarkwa, Obuasi, Bibiani, and Konongo.

Tropical Africa's diamonds are almost as valuable as its gold. They are mined with equal industriousness for use in industry and as precious jewels. More than 80 per cent of the world's diamonds come from tropical Africa. The diamond mines in Tanganyika alone are ranked among the largest in the world.

Of all the minerals useful to man, only coal and oil are scarce in tropical Africa. There are coal deposits in Nigeria, Tanganyika, and in Southern Rhodesia, which has the largest and best coal fields of the three countries.

Mining for diamonds in the Congo.
Belgian Government Information Center

The extensive forests of tropical Africa increase its natural wealth. Although their economic possibilities have perhaps been exaggerated, tree-covered lands are vitally important to the existence of the people, as well as to the land itself.

For most Africans, forests are the chief source of fuel, fodder for their cattle, and fertilizer for their farms. They need huge quantities of wood for cooking and for fuel to power railroad engines. Africans bring their cattle to forest areas to feed on leaves and fruit, during the seasons of drought when field grasses wither and die. They fertilize their land with wood ash, which is obtained by burning trees and brush. The finely powdered ash makes a good plant food as well as an ideal bed for starting seed.

Lumbering in the forests of tropical Africa.
Ivory Coast Service of Information

Lumberjacks in an African forest.

Ivory Coast Service of Information

A palm tree plantation in Africa surrounding the homes of workers.

A large percentage of the African's food is also provided by the forest. From wild and cultivated sections of the forest come such edible items as mangos, oranges, bananas, pawpaws (papayas), and cassavas. An edible fat is extracted from the seeds of the shea-butter tree. Salt is not too plentiful in tropical Africa. The majority of it is obtained from a shrub, *Salvadora persica*.

The forests are a convenient source of raw materials for building homes and for making household articles. Finally, they are producers of highly important commercial products. Natives make such personal possessions as pestles and mortars, spoons, dishes, matting, bedding, and even dugout canoes. Many trees and shrubs provide a variety of money crops such as gums, resins, dyes, fibers, flosses, palm oil, tung nuts, wattle (a source of tannin for curing leather), cacao, coffee, and rubber.

Rubber ranks particularly high economically. One of the largest rubber plantations in the African tropics is Firestone Plantations located in Liberia. It is operated by an American company, covers 100,000 planted acres, and includes some 12 million rubber trees. Rubber exports provide an important source of revenue for the Liberian government.

Rubber from Liberia en route to the United States.
Firestone News Service

A rubber tapper making
an incision in the bark
of a rubber tree. Latex
will flow down the cut
through a spout and into
the glass cup fixed to the
tree.

Below: *Liberian rubber
workers carrying pails of
rubber latex to a collecting station where it will
be weighed and shipped
by truck to a central
processing plant.*

Cocoa beans must dry in the sun for a week before they are ready for shipment. During this time workers using rakes frequently turn them.

Cacao (cocoa) is the biggest money-making crop in Ghana. The annual income derived from cocoa and cocoa products is over 150 million dollars. Coffee, another valuable bush plant, is the chief crop in Ethiopia where the plant is believed to have originated. *Coffea arabica,* the bush producing coffee beans, is said to have been first grown in the Ethiopian province of Kaffa, from which the word *coffee* is derived. Arab traders brought it to the Near East in the six-

Harvested cocoa pods are split open to remove the cocoa beans.

teenth century and not long after, coffee was introduced into Europe.

Lumbering is another source of income provided by the forests of tropical Africa. But logging is not easy in this part of the world. A given acre of forest land may contain only three or four trees of a single species that are worth cutting. The rest may have little or no commercial value. The worthwhile trees are seldom close together, thus increasing the cost of felling them. This is a feature common to lumbering throughout all the tropics.

Despite these drawbacks, the forests of tropical Africa do

produce a variety of timber of considerable commercial importance. Various species of mahogany are the best known. This wood is in great demand for fine cabinet work. Dibetou (African walnut), camphorwood, and Lolyondo are also much sought after.

The equatorial rain forests yield much timber useful in heavy construction work. The important trees in this group have such names as Kusia, Douka, Moabi, and Tau.

Tropical Africa's forests, as elsewhere, serve an additional valuable function to the land itself. They prevent erosion by torrential rains, retain moisture in the soil, provide nutrients and humus to the soil, and help economically important plants, such as cacao and banana, to flourish. These plants are given a shady canopy against a hot sun and a protective barrier against the wind.

A large lumber mill in Ghana.
Ghana Information Services

Economically important as Africa's forests are, it is farming on which most of the inhabitants depend for a living. Fortunately, they can grow just about every cultivatable crop there is. Of the world's 50 most valuable farm crops, 35 are grown commercially in the eastern section of tropical Africa alone: Kenya, Uganda, and Tanganyika among other countries. Plants thrive the year round. As soon as one crop is harvested, the soil is prepared for another. Continuous high heat

New farming methods being introduced in Ghana.

Ghana Information Services

and abundant moisture make plants grow faster than in countries of the temperate zones.

Cotton, peanuts, sisal, and tobacco are important money crops and are raised chiefly for export. Wheat and barley are also grown on a large scale and exported. In addition, Africans grow a number of other crops—cassava, plantains, grain, sorghums, and corn for their own use.

The last of tropical Africa's natural resources are its lakes and rivers. With the off-shore coastal waters on the east and west, they are an excellent source of fish. Lake Nyasa, in Southern Rhodesia, for example, is known to have more than 200 varieties of fish. The river and ocean waters are equally well populated; some have as many as 150 species.

Fishing, however, has not developed much as an industry. It is done on a commercial scale in only a few seacoast areas. Poor transportation facilities and lack of refrigeration equipment prevent a widespread distribution of fish. In addition, many tribes have a religious taboo against eating fish. Presumably, as the population of Africa increases and its need for a cheap, convenient source of protein increases too, fishing will be given more attention. One area where increased fishing activity is already underway is Ghana. Here the Fanti tribesmen, who have been fishermen for many generations, are being taught the techniques of large-scale tuna fishing.

The natural resources of tropical America are very much like those of Africa. This is especially true of the variety and extensiveness of its mineral deposits. Unlike Africa, however, tropical America's minerals have only been lightly tapped, chiefly because the problems of transporting them to market are great and the solutions costly. The mighty Andes, with peaks more than 18,000 feet high, and where much of the mineral wealth is located, are one obstacle. Another is the

An ore carrier from the United States loading iron ore at a Venezuelan port.

dense Amazon jungle. Such terrain makes the building of roads and railroads an engineer's nightmare.

Despite the mountains and jungles, however, ambitious efforts have been made to work the more accessible mineral deposits. In Chile the copper ore mines near the town of Chu-quicamata are being worked, as are desert areas containing large beds of nitrate, important in the manufacture of fertilizers. Chile is the only place in the world where this nitrate is found in such vast quantities. In the country also has been found commercially workable beds of sulphur, manganese, zinc, and lead.

In the mountains of neighboring Peru to the north are extensive veins of copper ore along with valuable beds of vana-

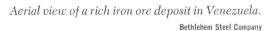

Aerial view of a rich iron ore deposit in Venezuela.

Bethlehem Steel Company

Bethlehem Steel Company

Iron ore from Venezuelan mines being stockpiled before shipment to steel furnaces in the United States.

dium and bismuth. Peru is the world's leading vanadium producer.

Bolivia ranks second in the world in the production of tin. The Bolivian government has long depended for revenue on the export of this metal.

Large oil fields, with their "black gold," have made Venezuela one of the wealthiest countries in tropical America. It is second only to the United States in petroleum production. Natural gas is also obtained in vast quantities. The discovery and development of these fabulously rich oil fields changed Venezuela from an agricultural to an industrial economy. The

Lake Maracaibo region in western Venezuela is one of the best oil producing centers.

Venezuela is also well endowed with high-grade iron ore. An estimated billion tons of ore are buried in the hills of the northern Guiana Highlands. The Bethlehem Steel Corporation of the United States was given the right by the Venezuelan government to develop those ore beds. A railroad and barge line are now used to transport the ore from the hills to the seacoast. From there large freighters carry the iron ore to Bethlehem's steel plant at Sparrows Point, Maryland.

Banana plantation in Costa Rica. The white puffs are overhead water sprinklers.

United Fruit Company

Special rail lines and mechanical equipment of a modern banana plantation.

Brazil is unquestionably the richest in natural resources of all the countries in tropical America. It is packed with vast and varied treasure. One need but mention a mineral and Brazil is almost certain to have it. In the southeastern part of the country are an estimated 13 billion tons of iron ore, one-quarter of the world's known reserve. Other minerals within the borders of this nation, which is almost as big as the United States, are coal, manganese, copper, bauxite, tin, co-

A banana port in Costa Rica.
United Fruit Company

balt, tungsten, and chrome. Veins of gold, silver, diamonds, and semiprecious stones, such as amethysts and aquamarines, are also mined commercially.

The forests of tropical America are extensive and rank in importance as a natural resource with the region's mineral deposits. The variety of its trees and bush plants yield both wild and cultivated products essential to the economic life of the inhabitants and much of the rest of the world as well. Some of the more important include coffee (Brazil is the world's number one producer), cinchona (a source of quinine), bananas, and cocoa, in the production of which Brazil ranks second.

Blossoms and fruit or "cherry" of a coffee tree. Seeds within the cherry are the coffee beans, two within each pod.

Pan-American Coffee Bureau

A Brazilian coffee plantation with the trees planted in contour fashion.

Despite the significant roles of mineral and forest resources, agriculture is the basis of tropical America's economy. The people depend on farm crops both for their own food and as a source of income. Among the more popular crops grown are cotton, manioc, sugar cane, rice, corn, and beans.

Green coffee being load-
ed aboard ship.

Depulped and washed
coffee beans are dried in
the open on sun-bathed
patios from four to eight
days. To insure even
drying the beans are
turned frequently.

A giant dredge working a tin deposit in Malaya.

Southeast Asia and the Indonesian archipelago also make substantial contributions to the natural wealth of the tropics. Tin and petroleum are the most important products. Tin is mined principally in the Malay Peninsula, southern Burma, and Thailand, and on the islands of Bangka and Billiton in Indonesia. Together, these places supply more than half the world's tin needs.

Most of the petroleum produced in southeast Asia comes from the island of Sumatra in Indonesia and from the northern and eastern parts of Borneo. Other, smaller oil fields are in central Burma and eastern Java.

Bauxite exists in the Rhio Archipelago, just south of Singapore. The Philippines has large deposits of manganese, gold, and chromite. Extensive fields of lead and silver are buried in the rugged hills of Burma. In addition to its tin ore deposits, the Malay Peninsula has valuable beds of tungsten. Iron ore deposits are scattered over a wide area but mined mainly in Malaya and the Philippine Islands. Like the rest of the tropics, southeast Asia has little coal. The only substantial deposits are in Tonkin in northern Vietnam, just on the fringe of the tropics.

Lush, widespread forests are also an important part of this natural resources picture. Forests in the Philippines provide the world with mahogany. From Java comes the lovely teak wood. Other tree products are resins, gums, rattan, and sandalwood.

Rubber leads the list of cultivated plant products. The rubber tree is not a native of Asia. Its original home is the tropical forest of Brazil. In 1877, specimens of the plant were brought to Malaya by way of England. The tree flourished and in a few decades Brazil lost its position as the world's leading natural rubber producer. Now ninety-five per cent of the world's natural rubber comes from southeast Asia. Most rubber trees used to be raised on large plantations, principally in Malaya, Ceylon, Sumatra, Borneo, and Java. Now small landowners in these countries produce the major part of the crop.

The cinchona tree (a source of quinine) was another South American plant which was brought to tropical Asia and thrived there. It grows on the volcanic slopes of western Java.

In the Philippine Islands there flourishes a particular species of native banana tree from which we get Manila hemp, a fiber used in the manufacture of rope and twine.

Plantation workers in Malaya pouring latex into a strainer.

Natural Rubber Bureau

Below: Rubber latex being piped aboard a freighter at a port in Malaya.

Natural Rubber Bureau

A Philippine farmer plowing his rice paddy with the help of a water buffalo.

Throughout tropical southeast Asia the ubiquitous coconut palm tree looms large in the economy. As we know, it provides food, clothing and shelter, as well as copra, a valuable export. The tree thrives far and wide over this part of the tropics, from Ceylon to the Marquesas Islands in the south central Pacific.

Tropical southeast Asia has two hundred million inhabitants. Most are farmers who raise rice as their principal crop. The chief rice producing countries are Malaya, Burma, Thailand, and South Vietnam. Generally, the surplus is exported, providing a much needed source of income.

Rice culture has been practiced here for centuries and with such skill that the lands have never lost their fertility. Rice plants are grown in irrigated fields, called paddies. After one crop has been harvested, a second is often planted. The water buffalo, a powerful, plodding creature, does the heavy work of plowing the water-logged soil of the paddies.

Other agricultural products include yams, corn, peanuts, sweet potatoes, tobacco, sugar cane, tea, coffee, cassava, and bananas. Sugar cane, like rice, has been raised in this part of the world for many centuries. Tea is grown principally in Ceylon, Java, and western Sumatra. Java is also a coffee growing center. Cassava, widely eaten by the natives, is exported to countries in the higher latitudes. Here the people know it as tapioca.

As in other regions of the tropics, the people of tropical Asia have not taken full advantage of the seas' resources. However, in Java and Thailand they have built a number of fish farms, fresh water ponds, enclosed by walls, in which various species of fish are bred, fattened, and "harvested," like beef cattle on a range. The ponds are stocked with fry

United Nations Office of Public Information

Raising fish in ponds for food is popular in tropical southeast Asia. Natives are shown carrying fry in baskets.

and when these mature the fish are eaten by the farmers and also sold.

Although minerals and forests endow the tropics with enormous riches, it is agriculture on which most inhabitants depend for their existence. And agricultural practices in many parts of the tropics are quite unlike those employed in countries of the temperate zone. The methods are simple, centuries old and symbolized by the digging stick, often the farmer's only tool. In many instances farms consist of a clearing hacked out of the forest, since these lands are considered the most fertile. Trees too big to cut down with an axe are girdled and allowed to die. When these are dead and dried they are set afire. All cut trees and bushes are put to the torch not only to dispose of them but to provide fertilizer.

Once the land is cleared, it is ready for planting. The men use a simple stick or hoe for putting in seeds or young seedlings. A common practice, particularly among African farmers, is to poke a hole in the ground with the digging stick, drop in the seed, and kick or hoe the soil over it. After the seed is planted, the success of a crop is in the hands of nature. Except for weeding from time to time once the seed has sprouted, the farmers do little else. If there is ample but not excessive rain, and if there are few insects, the crop will usually be a good one.

Farms created and worked in this manner are good for only three years. After that the soil is exhausted. Then the farmers pull up stakes and move to another part of their country, repeating the process of clearing and burning the forest land.

The lush plant life in the tropics has led people to believe that the soil is inexhaustible and a kind of magical substance capable of making even a clothespin sprout. Forests with their luxuriant plant life have been primarily responsible for this impression. Here nature has provided ideal growing conditions, not the least of which is the replacement of soil nutrients by decaying vegetation. But an entirely different state of affairs exists on cleared lands. In these areas the soil nutrients quickly disappear, largely carried off by heavy rains. Farmers rarely if ever return these to the soil in the form of fertilizer. As a result, they are continually forced to seek new fertile lands.

While this simple agricultural system, so common in a number of tropical countries, may have had some merit in the past, it is not adequate today. For the amount of physical labor involved in tilling the land, returns are pitifully small.

Farmers in India plowing the soil with buffalo power.

World Health Organization (Eric Schwab)

Tractor-drawn plows undergoing tests at an experimental farming station in the Congo.

More serious is the damage inflicted on precious soil resources. Exhausted land, if not permanently scarred by erosion, requires at least fifteen years to return to fertility. If the tropics are to be able to properly feed a growing population, it is inevitable that the current farming methods must undergo drastic change.

6

MOSQUITOES, WORMS,
AND TROPICAL DISEASES

AMONG THE THINGS the first European
visitors to the tropics were quick to learn was the ease with
which a variety of deadly diseases could be acquired. Thereafter the tropics gained a reputation for being unhealthy.
Medical science has long since eliminated or controlled a
number of the diseases but others remain, particularly in the
less-developed areas. It is primarily because of these diseases
that life in the tropics is still considered more hazardous than
anywhere else in the world.

Of course, countries outside the tropics have their own
formidable lists of illnesses to plague man. However, in the
tropics one is exposed both to these and to native diseases.
Tuberculosis and pneumonia, common in the higher latitudes, are equally at home in the tropics.

Consistently high temperature, excessive moisture, and the
lack of adequate water purification equipment and sanitary
facilities help make the tropics a particularly favorable place
for diseases. High heat and an overabundance of water alone
create ideal spawning conditions for swarms of insects and

disease-causing bacteria. Stagnant pools, swamps, ponds, marshes, shallow wells, and pits are some of the main breeding places. These are the favorite haunts of the anopheles mosquitoes which transmit malaria, the greatest scourge of the tropics. Other disease-causing insects are houseflies, sandflies, tsetse flies, ticks, gnats, mites, lice, and the reduviid or "kissing" bug.

Bacteria-laden drinking water is the source of numerous tropical illnesses, some extremely serious. These include,

W.H.O. is waging a vigorous educational campaign throughout the tropics to eradicate yaws. Photos showing characteristics of the disease are an important tool and are here being examined by an African mother.

World Health Organization (Paul Almasy)

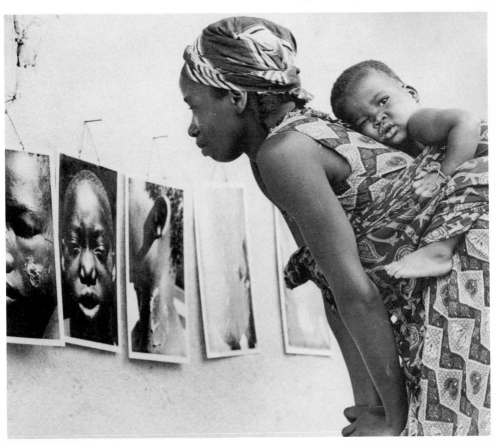

common diarrheas, amoebic dysentery, bacillary dysentery, typhoid fever, cholera, and guinea-worm infections.

Sanitary facilities in many parts of the tropics, especially among the more primitive peoples, are crude or nonexistent. This, coupled with poor personal hygiene, increases the

Africans line up for examination for possible signs of yaws.

World Health Organization (Dr. Hackett)

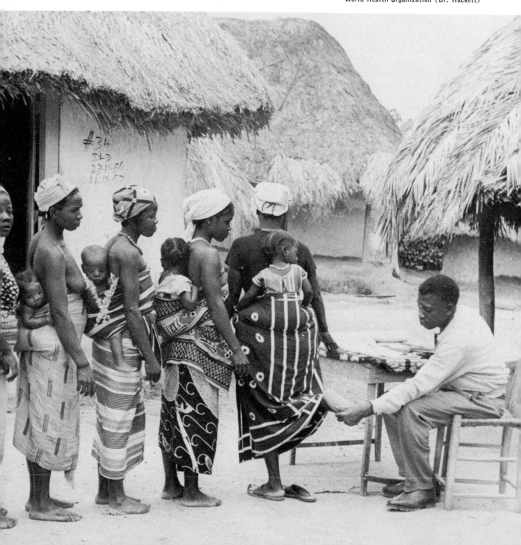

A medical expert of a W.H.O. health team administering smallpox vaccinations to a Colombian family.

*Medical team vac-
cinating inhabi-
tants in a remote
Colombian village.*

chances for germs to breed and weakens the resistance of the inhabitants to illness.

Of the many diseases to which the people of the tropics are exposed, malaria is the most common. This illness is not confined to hot climates, but occurs in a number of other places, including the southern part of the United States. Medical authorities estimate that malaria attacks about one-third of the human race, killing two million people and afflicting two hundred million others annually. India, with its vast population, provides nearly half this number of fatalities.

Liberian village chief and family watch a member of W.H.O. health team spray house with DDT in fight against malaria.

Almost everyone in the tropics has been stricken with malaria at one time. Those who survive a serious attack go through life physically weakened. Many become chronic sufferers, experiencing attacks of fever, chills, loss of appetite,

African mother swallowing anti-malaria tablet given by member of W.H.O. medical team.

World Health Organization (Paul Almasy)

and energy. Children in many lands form the largest group of victims.

Malaria is especially prevalent in low-lying areas which are consistently warm and humid. It strikes exceptionally hard in localities where there is a distinct rainy season. Then the ground becomes saturated with moisture and covered with countless pools and ponds, breeding grounds for the anopheles mosquitoes.

Until the beginning of this century, science knew little about the cause of malaria. In 1897–1899 an English medical research specialist, Dr. Ronald Ross, found that a parasite thriving within a mosquito's body brought on the disease. The mosquito itself merely furnishes transportation for the parasite and provides the puncturing tool by which it is injected into the human body.

If this malaria-laden mosquito bites a dog, or cow, or any other four-legged creature, the parasite it transplants will die, although it will infect poultry or birds. In the human blood stream the malaria parasite propagates itself.

The oldest and most effective remedy for malaria is quinine, obtained from the bark of the cinchona tree. Modern medical researchers have also created numerous synthetic drugs. Some are known by such names as Aralen, Camoquin,

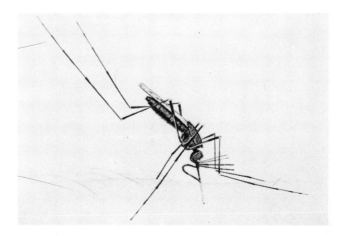

Anopheles mosquito.

Communicable Disease Center,
Atlanta, Georgia U.S.D.H.E.W.

Daraprim, and Atebrine. During World War II, when thousands of American soldiers were sent to the southwest Pacific and other malaria-infested areas, Atebrine was an important and regular item in their daily diet.

Strenuous efforts are being made throughout the tropics to check and eradicate malaria. The World Health Organization of the United Nations is leading the fight. Under its guidance, programs aimed at destroying the breeding places of the anopheles mosquitoes with insecticides are being carried out in many tropical countries. At the same time, WHO is trying to convince the people that it is important for them to take antimalaria drugs regularly.

The struggle against malaria is also being pressed in the field of research. A new drug has been created, known as CI-501, which when perfected is expected to provide protection against malaria with a single injection for as long as a year.

Sleeping sickness is another tropical disease. While it is not so widespread as malaria, it is every bit as vicious. Two types, Gambian and Rhodesian, attack human beings. Of these, Rhodesian is the more serious. Sleeping sickness is confined to tropical Africa and to a small area in South America. It is spread by the blood-sucking tsetse fly, which breeds in moist, shady places. The insect, of which there are about twenty known species, is about the size of an ordinary housefly and brownish in color. If the adult fly finds a steady supply of blood, it can live for many months. Its lifespan is unusually long for an insect. The tsetse itself does not cause sleeping sickness. It is the carrier of a tiny organism, the trypanosome, which actually performs the deadly work in man and animals.

Both eastern and western portions of tropical Africa have

tsetse flies, but the western is more heavily infested. During the years explorers were making journeys into the African interior, the tsetse fly proved a formidable enemy. Once its habit of biting only in the daytime was discovered, explorers traveled at night and as swiftly as possible through areas known to be inhabited by this dreadful pest.

The tsetse fly's bite does not have an immediate effect. It takes time, sometimes months, for the parasite to become established in the bloodstream. The first clear sign is an overwhelming lethargy and a constant desire to sleep. When some of the African slaves were first brought to America, they were healthy and vigorous. But after a few months in the new world, many suddenly became slow and sleepy. They were thought to be suffering from a kind of homesickness. Actually, the slaves were victims of the tsetse fly and only after the long ocean voyage did signs of the illness begin to show.

Often during the final stages of sleeping sickness the victim will become mentally deranged. Those who survive the

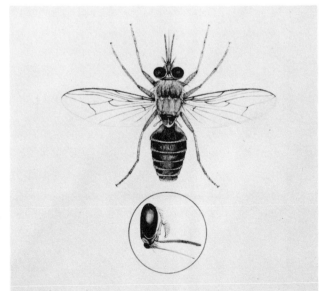

Tsetse fly.

Communicable Disease Center,
Atlanta, Georgia U.S.D.H.E.W.

illness usually remain mentally unbalanced for the remainder of their lives.

Until the creation of new and potent drugs, such as Tryparsamide and Peutamidine, sleeping sickness was almost always fatal. Now, with their help, doctors are at last able to offer victims some hope of recovery.

In addition to the use of drugs, an attack is being made on the disease at its source. Tsetse fly breeding places are being sprayed with DDT and other insecticides. Infected areas are also being burned over. Cattle and wild animals, also frequent victims of the fly, are systematically destroyed, since they are one of the chief ways the disease is carried from an infected to a noninfected area. Consequently, thousands of Africa's big game have been killed, a tactic that has dismayed many game conservationists.

The task of eradicating sleeping sickness from tropical Africa, borne mostly by medical experts of the World Health Organization, is beginning to produce results. The tsetse fly has been eliminated from a vast portion of Africa. At one time the disease it spread raged from Zululand in the south to the Sahara Desert in the north, an area of more than 4,500,000 square miles. Nor does Africa experience enormous sleeping sickness epidemics as in former years. In the decade from 1896 to 1906, for example, 200,000 Africans died (because of the tsetse fly) in Uganda alone. Now, in all of tropical Africa the annual average of deaths due to sleeping sickness is 20,000.

Yellow fever is another serious health hazard in the tropics. Like malaria, it is common throughout the region. The disease is caused by a virus, carried by the mosquito *Aëdes aegypti.*

The yellow fever attack on man varies in form. At times the

infection is so mild that symptoms can hardly be detected. But more frequently it strikes swiftly and with great severity. Its victims are usually subjected to a raging fever at first and then stomach and kidney bleeding. Within two weeks the disease will have run its course. If the victim survives, he is immune from further attacks.

It was yellow fever that defeated the efforts of French engineers in their attempt to build a canal across the Isthmus of Panama. In the steaming forests, hundreds of workers lost their lives to the attacks of fever-bearing mosquitoes. American engineers, who later took over the construction project succeeded, but only because medical science had learned how to hold yellow fever in check. For this knowledge, thanks had to go to a United States Army medical research worker, Dr. Walter Reed.

Shortly after the end of the Spanish-American War in 1898, Dr. Reed was placed at the head of a medical commission and sent to Cuba to see what could be done about improving health conditions. Yellow fever was one of the diseases that plagued the island. Havana, a notorious center for the disease, was considered a most unhealthy city. Because of yellow fever's widespread incidence, Dr. Reed and his colleagues decided to concentrate their attention on it.

Following a series of dramatic experiments, Dr. Reed showed beyond doubt that the disease was caused by *Aëdes aegypti*. After that it was a comparatively easy matter to keep yellow fever in check simply by destroying the breeding grounds of the mosquito. In a few years the disease was wiped out, not only in Cuba, but also in the entire Caribbean region.

Nowadays, people are protected from yellow fever by vaccination, as well as by the destruction of spawning places. But in parts of tropical South America and Africa, where it is difficult to locate all the breeding areas, control measures are still not completely effective. As a result, periodic outbreaks of yellow fever do occur, and before they can be checked, deaths result.

Strange worms do almost as much damage as mosquitoes. The nematode worm is responsible for a whole family of diseases which are lumped under the name filariasis. The more dangerous of these result in tumors, blindness, and a grotesque sickness known as elephantiasis. Common to almost all the tropics, elephantiasis causes enormous enlargement of various parts of a victim's body. Feet and legs are most often attacked and these take on the appearance of an elephant's extremities and a hardening of the skin.

W.H.O. zoologist searching for snails that carry bilharziasis, a disease common in many parts of the tropics.

World Health Organization

W.H.O. team (to the right) checks pool of water in Somalia for mosquito larvae which may carry malaria.

World Health Organization

Rice cultivator in the Philippines clearing his canal of aquatic plants on which snails which may carry bilharziasis thrive.

Burmese children being given pills in W.H.O. program to control leprosy.

World Health Organization (B. Scheidgger)

The Guinea worm, another form of filariasis, is also capable of doing serious harm. It often causes blindness after entering the human body.

These disease-bearing worms are carried mainly by contaminated drinking water. It is estimated that in tropical Africa alone fifty million inhabitants suffer from some form of filariasis.

One of the most dreadful tropical diseases is leprosy. It is sometimes referred to as Hansen's disease, after the discoverer of the organism that causes the malady. Leprosy is contagious and makes necessary the separation of the infected from the noninfected. As with sleeping sickness, those who contract leprosy are not aware that they have it until several months, or even years, have passed. It is a cruel disease that leaves victims pitifully disfigured as it progresses through the body, and eventually causes death. Before the creation of sulfa and antibiotic drugs, doctors could do little to help lepers. Today, the disease is successfully checked with these medicines except in its most advanced stages.

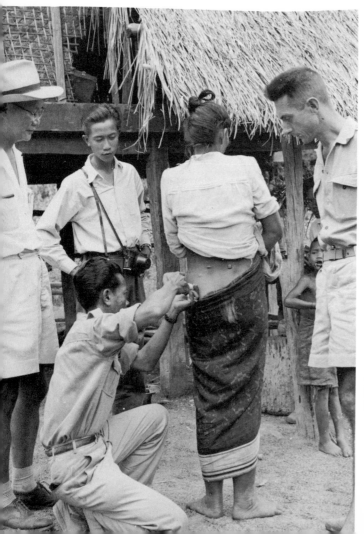

Laotian being treated for yaws with a shot of penicillin.

World Health Organization

Leprosy exists throughout the tropics, although in Africa the number of victims is particularly high. About two and a half million of its inhabitants suffer from leprosy.

Yaws is a disease familiar to widely scattered sections of the tropics. Not as serious as leprosy, it nevertheless can cause permanent disfigurement of the face, damage to the brain, and it may even prove fatal. It is especially common among children. Yaws is believed to be caused mainly by a tiny organism, *Treponema pertenue*, found in filth. This and poor personal hygiene are the primary reasons for its widespread occurrence.

The construction of better sanitary facilities, campaigns seeking to improve hygiene habits and the use of penicillin are successfully reducing the incidence of yaws.

Burmese boy being examined for tuberculosis by health assistant.
World Health Organization (Homer Page)

Along with the diseases described so far, inhabitants of the tropics also have to watch out for dysentery, typhoid fever, hookworm, and ordinary poor health brought on by poor diet. Nutritional deficiencies are very common, chiefly among children, in all the underdeveloped countries. A particularly

School children in Colombia receiving smallpox vaccination.

World Health Organization (Paul Almasy)

severe form of malnutrition, called kwashiorkor, is caused by a protein deficiency. Many children are victims of it and show its effects with swollen heads and bellies, and sunken chests. Milk and good food are normally all that is needed to bring about their recovery.

Constant exposure to this army of diseases places a heavy burden on the lives of millions of people. Particularly in tropical Africa does man have to become used to one illness after the other. He considers himself lucky if he lives to fifty-five or sixty.

Nor is man the only victim. Domestic animals and the beasts of the jungle are also susceptible to disease. A whole host of maladies keep African cattle scrawny and of little value as food suppliers. One of the most serious, which also strikes wild animals, is trypanosomiasis, caused by that scourge of the African tropics, the tsetse fly. Because of this insect many areas of tropical Africa are unsuitable for raising cattle.

Other cattle diseases include rinderpest, pleura-pneumonia, anthrax, blackleg, and tick fever. These are particularly prevalent in the African tropics. In Ethiopia more than a million cattle die annually from rinderpest alone.

Medical science has long been interested in tropical diseases. The roll call of medical research specialists who spent a lifetime studying these illnesses is long and illustrious. It is primarily because of their patient labors that a number of these diseases have been brought under partial or complete control. Outstanding among the pioneers were such men as Dr. Patrick Mason, often called the "father of tropical medicine" following his research that showed mosquitoes are one of the main carriers of tropical diseases; Dr. Ronald Ross whom we met earlier; and Hideyo Noguchi who found additional scientific knowledge on yellow fever.

Besides the medical scientists, there were a host of other men, doctors and humanitarians, who became interested in tropical diseases. A few of these dedicated individuals achieved world fame as a result of their work.

The first was Father Joseph Damien de Veuster, better known simply as Father Damien. Although trained to minister to the spirit rather than the flesh, this Roman Catholic priest performed heroic services by bringing comfort to sufferers of leprosy. It was in a leper colony on the island of Molokai, Hawaii, that Father Damien carried on his activities.

Father Damien first came to the Hawaiian Islands in 1864 as a young priest from Belgium. After some years of caring for the ordinary religious needs of the islanders, he volunteered to work among the forgotten lepers of Molokai. Shocked by both their appearance and the primitive conditions in which they lived, he decided that he would spend the rest of his days doing what he could to ease the hardships of these neglected people. He helped to dress their wounds; he encouraged them to build decent shelters; he taught them how to plant more and better crops. In the course of his inspiring work, Father Damien changed the atmosphere from one of black despair to cheerfulness and hope.

At last the dreaded day came when Father Damien was told that he had leprosy. He left Molokai for Honolulu and hospital treatment. But the disease had progressed too far and could no longer be checked. With the knowledge that he was incurably ill, Father Damien returned to his leper friends on Molokai, and died there in 1889.

A healer of the sick in the tropics today is Dr. Gordon S. Seagrave, known as the Burma Surgeon. Dr. Seagrave was born in Burma of a Baptist missionary family. Following his graduation from medical school he chose to go into the remote hills of this tropical country, where hospital and medical facilities were almost nonexistent, to bring aid and comfort to the sick and injured.

Dr. Seagrave has labored untiringly for forty years. Single-handed, he has brought the knowledge and skill of modern medicine to thousands of Burmese suffering from all sorts of illnesses. At the hospital which Dr. Seagrave founded at Namhkham, 6,000 or more in-patients are treated during the course of a year as well as 10,000 others who, after treatment, are able to go home. Burmese come to the American doctor from as far away as a hundred miles. Now helped by an assistant doctor, Dr. Seagrave performs about 1,500 operations a year. In addition to his regular medical duties, he has trained many nurses as surgical and hospital assistants.

During World War II Burma was the center of fierce fighting between the Japanese and Allied forces. Dr. Seagrave's tiny medical oasis, which he had created with so much difficulty, was demolished. Undaunted, he built a new hospital, bigger and better equipped than the first one, at the end of hostilities.

Dr. Albert Schweitzer is undoubtedly the most famous of the present day doctors who have gone to the tropics to aid the sick. Born on January 14, 1875 in the tiny Alsace village of Kaysersberg, Albert Schweitzer came from a deeply religious family. His father was a Protestant minister in Günsbach, a nearby village. Shortly after Albert was born, the elder Schweitzer moved his family to Günsbach and Albert grew up there in a home where the importance of helping those in less fortunate circumstances was constantly emphasized.

Largely because of his family background and training,

Albert Schweitzer seemed destined to spend his life aiding others. As a young man he devoted a number of years to the ministry. But this did not satisfy his great inner urge to serve his fellow man. Then one day, while wondering what he would do with his life, he came across a pamphlet published by the Paris Missionary Society. It was an appeal for young men to join the society to work among the natives of equatorial Africa. Many of these people were dying from a variety of tropical diseases because of the absence of medical help. Immediately Albert Schweitzer sensed that here was the opportunity for which he had long been looking.

Within a short time he became a member of the society. The decision was not easy. He was already thirty years old and well-launched on several careers—as a minister, as a musician (he was a talented organist), and as a writer on philosophical subjects. Furthermore, in order to equip himself better for work among the people of Africa, he had to acquire a medical degree. This meant spending a number of years in a medical school. Despite his family's and his friends' pleas that he abandon the idea, Albert went ahead with his plans.

After six years of arduous study, the young missionary obtained the title of physician in 1911. During this period he had displayed the tremendous energy that was to be characteristic of him throughout his life. Despite the long hours devoted to his studies, Albert Schweitzer kept up many of his former activities, particularly preaching and playing the organ. In 1913 his preparations were at last completed and he set out for the equatorial forests of Africa.

Dr. Schweitzer started his now famous jungle hospital at Lambaréné in Gabon, formerly a colony of France. The beginning was heartbreaking. Facilities were the crudest—

an abandoned chicken shed served as an operating room—
and the newly trained doctor was overwhelmed by the great
numbers of sick who came to him for help. Word of mouth
and jungle communications soon made the white doctor's
presence known for miles around. But most difficult of all,
perhaps, were the adjustments which Dr. Schweitzer himself
had to make to his new and utterly strange surroundings.
Not the least was to learn to bear up under the exhausting
heat.

Dr. Schweitzer persisted, however, and as he became
deeply involved in his work, no longer noticed the hardships.
People came to his little hospital in dugout canoes, on foot,
and on litters. Those who could paid the doctor with food
or forest products, with sheep, goats, and chickens. Dr.
Schweitzer's hospital became a mecca for sick Africans.

*A modern hospital maintained by the Firestone Company in Liberia for its
rubber plantation workers.*

Firestone News Service

After more than 45 years of ministering to the sick, Dr. Schweitzer's fame has spread throughout the world. Although seemingly blessed with boundless good health and energy, he found it increasingly difficult to care for all those who sought his help. Others came to assist him so that now Dr. Schweitzer's hospital is staffed by a small group of devoted doctors and nurses.

There are other skilled medical workers laboring in the tropics with equal unselfishness and intensity. They have formed isolated beachheads in the vast tropical world as they fight the many-pronged onslaughts of an invisible enemy. Dedicated to their work, these doctors are showing that, despite the terrible harm so many tropic illnesses are capable of inflicting, they can be successfully challenged with the help of modern medical knowledge and drugs.

7

THE TROPICS
SURGE AHEAD

THE TROPICS are destined for great changes in the years ahead. Especially in the more backward lands is there an irresistible urge to catch up with the advanced nations. A number of changes, which the restlessness of the people is initiating, are already in full swing. The most spectacular are political.

During the European explorations of the sixteenth, seventeenth, and eighteenth centuries, many tropical lands were seized as colonies. For decades their political and economic affairs were controlled by outsiders, mostly Europeans. The colonial period has nearly ended, particularly in many sections of tropical Africa, and southeast Asia.

Since World War II millions of people in these two regions have gained their independence and old colonies have become new nations. More than thirty have come into existence and have joined the United Nations as full-fledged members. Most of these countries made the transition from colonial rule to self-rule with little difficulty, mainly because there were trained leaders ready to take over the reins of government. In some instances, however, where experienced leaders were lacking or where native rivals struggled for control of the government, strife and chaos resulted. This happened in the former Belgian Congo where United Nations forces intervened to restore order.

Many of the new nations as well as those that have long enjoyed self-government are underdeveloped by comparison

A scene in the Legislative Assembly of the Republic of Somalia. Mural behind the President's chair symbolizes Somali unity.

United Nations

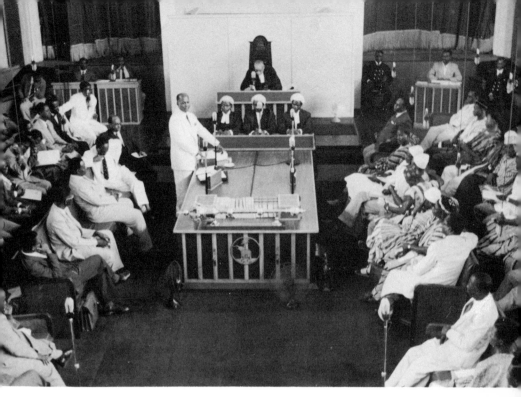

Above: *A legislative meeting of a newborn African nation.*

The future of tropical Africa is in the hands of such young men as these.

with other countries outside the tropics. This has started important changes in the social and economic fields. Almost all of these countries have ambitious plans to improve the welfare of the inhabitants. Some of the goals being sought include better homes for the people, control and elimination

Members of Parliament meeting in the Republic of the Congo.
United Nations

Construction of new houses in tropical Africa.

A new shipping port under construction in Burundi on Lake Tanganyika.

of diseases, development of industries to provide more opportunities for work, the construction of roads, and the modernization of communications.

Unfortunately, the majority of these tropical nations lack the financial strength to carry out the improvement programs without assistance. Equally serious is their scarcity of trained professional and technical personnel needed to operate expanded government services and to bring new knowledge and skills to the people. Because of these weaknesses, a variety of aid from a number of sources is being extended to these countries and, despite difficulties, progress is being made.

A powerful tractor clearing the land for a new railway line in Tanganyika.

United Nations

The Markala dam in the Niger River, one of the largest dams in the world built exclusively for irrigation.

The United Nations is playing a major role in helping these tropical lands to achieve their aspirations. Financial loans on easy terms, and outright grants in some cases, are being given; people with professional and technical skills in such fields as government, education, medicine, and agriculture are being sent to wherever they are requested.

Industrially advanced nations—the United States, Great Britain, France, and Russia among others—are also contributing assistance. One of the unique forms of aid being provided by the United States is through its Peace Corps. This is a group of young men and women and older individuals with varied professional and technical abilities. Within the framework of the improvement programs of the individual tropical countries to which they are sent, Peace Corps members are

New bridge being constructed in Cameroons.
Twentieth Century Fund

John and Bini Moss from Black Star

An American Peace Corps member in a chemistry class in Ghana.

attempting to bring some immediate benefits to the people by helping in the construction of homes, bridges, irrigation ditches and in the destruction of breeding places of disease-bearing insects. They are also engaged in teaching, nursing, and agricultural activities. In brief, Peace Corps members are partially filling the gap in trained manpower until native personnel are available to take over the many tasks. In this connection, thousands of qualified men and women from tropical nations are attending universities and technical schools in the more advanced countries.

The ultimate success of the improvement programs now underway in the underdeveloped lands will depend to a

4-H Club members being shown how to test the soil in their school garden by a Peace Corps Volunteer.

great extent on the countries' economic strength and the changes expected to occur in that field. Since natural resources are a key factor in the economy of many of these nations, they will continue to play a dominant role. Tin, copper, nickel, and iron, among others, have long been valuable exports. They promise to become even more so in the future as sources for these minerals outside the tropics dwindle or become exhausted.

The United States, which at one time had little need to import iron ore, is already tapping tropical deposits for immense quantities of this essential metal. This trend will continue as the industrial pace in the more highly developed countries is stepped up and raw materials are required.

The future importance of natural resources in the tropics will also increase as the countries there strive to become more industrialized. Their own factories will then need raw materials for manufactured products.

There are other aspects of the expected economic changes in the tropics, such as the development of water power. This will be essential if industrialization is to increase. As we know, the region is deficient in supplies of coal. But ample water resources in many tropical lands make a good substitute. In those lands where this energy source has already been exploited a degree of industrialization exists. This and the use of hydroelectric power for raising living standards in the household have resulted in the planning of many new hydroelectric projects. A great deal of this engineering activity is centered in tropical Africa.

For example, the government of the Republic of Guinea has plans for harnessing the lower reaches of the Konkouré River. When finished this power station is expected to generate about 3 billion kilowatt hours of electricity. Most of this energy will be used to operate an aluminum factory, since great quantities of electricity are needed to transform the bauxite ore into usable aluminum metal. Still another large hydroelectric plant is being considered for the Inga Rapids portion of the Congo River. To be located between the Congo cities of Léopoldville and Matadi, this electric power generating station is designed to produce in excess of 25 million kilowatts, 20 times the power generated by the giant Hoover Dam in the United States.

Part of a hydroelectric power station in the Republic of Rwanda.

United Nations

Some tropical countries, particularly in South America, have, in addition to water resources, abundant supplies of petroleum and natural gas for the production of electrical power. Venezuela has vast amounts of these fuels, so too has Brazil.

For the more distant future, atomic energy may be available to the lands of the tropics. It has the potential of outstripping water, petroleum, and natural gas in importance as a power producer. Southeast Asia may be ideal for this modern form of energy since it is poor in both coal and water power.

Still another feature of economic change in the tropics will involve the region's extensive timber lands. Through the magic of chemistry, their potential future value promises to be enormously increased over what it is at present. One development toward that end is a chemical process that will soon make possible the conversion of hardwood trees into pulpwood for the manufacture of paper and paper products. Until now only the softwood trees of the higher latitudes have been converted for this purpose. Once this process is perfected, it will be much more profitable to exploit tropical forests since it will no longer be necessary to be selective in the cutting of trees.

Over a longer time range, the science of chemistry may do even greater things for the forests of the tropics. Predictions are being made that someday tropical timber lands may be converted into huge outdoor factories producing such diverse products as cellulose (the raw material of synthetic fibers and plastics), alcohol, lubricants, insecticides, and paint. Some chemists even see the time when the trees will be transformed into valuable foodstuffs via the test tube.

Agriculture promises to contribute its share to the future economic picture of the tropics. Just as science is on the

Firestone News Service
Dwellings of rubber plantation workers in Liberia.

verge of altering drastically the importance of the forests, so too does it promise to revolutionize tropical agriculture. From study and experiment will come new farming methods especially tailored to the climate conditions of the tropics. These will be of such a nature that scorching sun and torrential rains will no longer be the hazards they are today, particularly in the conservation of precious topsoil. Adequate plant protection will also be devised against the great variety and numbers of destructive insects.

Should these developments materialize, tomorrow's farmer in the tropics may well become an expert in mechanized farming and in the use of chemical fertilizers and other chemicals for battling weeds, insects, and plant diseases. Many of the current primitive practices such as burning over a farming area and using a planting stick will be discarded. In some parts of the tropics today, newer agricultural methods are already being employed and proving highly successful.

The political, economic, and social upheavals taking place throughout much of the tropics are not confined to that region alone. Similar activities are going on in other parts of the world, too. But in the tropics the changes are on a far larger scale and more dramatic and drastic. This is because the needs are so much greater than elsewhere. While significant

Government buildings on the Plaza of the Three Powers in Brasilia, the capital of Brazil. Brasilia was carved out of barren, tropical wasteland.

Ministerio Das Relacoes Exteriores

Above: *Apartment building in Nigeria.*

Young men being trained for office positions in Liberia.

progress has been made toward improving the social and economic standing of this region, much still remains to be accomplished. However long the journey may be, the future is bright with the promise that the tropics will become a healthier, wealthier area, capable of supporting in far more comfortable circumstances than now its millions of inhabitants.

BIBLIOGRAPHY

BOOKS

Bourlière, F. and others. *The Tropics.* New York: Alfred A. Knopf, Inc., 1957.

Burdick, E. *Blue of Capricorn.* Boston: Houghton Mifflin Co., 1961.

Debenham, F. *Discovery and Exploration.* New York: Doubleday & Company, Inc., 1960.

Freuchen, P. *Peter Freuchen's Book of the Seven Seas.* New York: Julian Messner, 1957.

Gourou, P. and Laborde, E. D. *Tropical World.* New York: Longmans Green & Co., Inc., 1958.

Grzimek, Bernhard and Michael. *Serengeti Shall Not Die.* New York: E. P. Dutton & Co., Inc., 1961.

Kimble, G. H. T. *Tropical Africa.* 2 vols. New York: Twentieth Century Fund, 1960.

Linton, R., Ed. *Most of the World.* New York: Columbia University Press, 1949.

Oliver, D. L. *Pacific Islands.* Cambridge, Mass.: Harvard University Press, 1951.

Robequain, C. *Malaya, Indonesia, Borneo, and the Philippines.* 2nd ed. New York: Longmans Green & Co., Inc., 1958.

ARTICLES

Gilliard, E. Thomas. "Exploring New Britain's Land of Fire," *National Geographic Magazine,* February, 1961.

Huxley, Elspeth. "Africa's First Loyalty," *New York Times Magazine,* September 18, 1960.

Kenney, Nathaniel T. "The Winds of Freedom Stir a Continent," *National Geographic Magazine,* September, 1960.

Leakey, L. S. B. "Finding the World's Earliest Man," *National Geographic Magazine,* September, 1960.

Rodger, George and Jinx. "Where Elephants Have Right of Way," *National Geographic Magazine,* September, 1960.

Scofield, John. "Haiti—West Africa in the West Indies," *National Geographic Magazine,* February, 1961.

Ward, Barbara. "Change Comes to Africa's Villages," *New York Times Magazine,* November 19, 1961.

"Africa," *Holiday,* Vol. 25, No. 4, April, 1959.

"Cambodia," *Focus,* Vol. XII, No. 8, American Geographical Society.

"Ethiopia," *Focus,* Vol. V, No. 10, American Geographical Society.

"Ghana," *Focus,* Vol. IX, No. 8, American Geographical Society.

"India's Languages and Religions," *Focus,* Vol. VI, No. 6, American Geographical Society.

"Indonesia," *Focus,* Vol. VII, No. 4, American Geographical Society.

"India's Industrial Growth," *Focus,* Vol. VI, No. 9, American Geographical Society.

"Malaya," *Focus,* Vol. IX, No. 2, American Geographical Society.

"Malaya—A New Independent Nation," Department of State Publication, No. 6714.

"Resources of the Tropics—I-Africa," *Focus,* Vol. III, No. 4, American Geographical Society.

"Resources of the Tropics—II-South America," *Focus,* Vol. III, No. 8, American Geographical Society.

"Resources of the Tropics—III-Southeast Asia," *Focus,* Vol. IV, No. 6, American Geographical Society.

"South East Asia," *World Health,* Vol. XIV, No. 1, January-February, 1961.

"Tanganyika," *Focus,* Vol. XII, No. 10, American Geographical Society.

"Thailand," *Focus,* Vol. XII, No. 6, American Geographical Society.

"The World of the South Pacific," *Holiday,* Vol. 28, No. 4, October, 1960.

"The World of the South Pacific," *Holiday,* Vol. 28, No. 5, November, 1960.

"Venezuela," *Focus,* Vol. II, No. 9, American Geographical Society.

"Western New Guinea," *Focus,* Vol. XII, No. 5, American Geographical Society.

CHRONOLOGY

1492–1503 CHRISTOPHER COLUMBUS MAKES FOUR VOYAGES TO THE AMERICAN TROPICS.

1497   John Cabot, a Venetian sailing for the English, reaches Canada.

1497   Amerigo Vespucci reveals he reached the mainland of the New World before Columbus.

1498 VASCO DA GAMA REACHES CALICUT, INDIA.

1510 AFFONSO DE ALBUQUERQUE SEIZES GOA, INDIA, CONTINUES VOYAGE TO EAST INDIES.

1513   Juan Ponce de Leon discovers and names Florida.

1513   Balboa discovers South Sea—called Pacific by Magellan.

1517   Martin Luther, an Augustinian monk, breaks with the Church of Rome.

1519 FERDINAND MAGELLAN EMBARKS ON VOYAGE AROUND THE WORLD.

1519   Hernando Cortes begins conquest of Mexico.

1520   Magellan discovers Strait of Magellan and Tierra del Fuego.

1524   Verrazano—Italian mariner sailing for France, reaches America and is believed to have entered New York Harbor.

1531–35   Francisco Pizzaro conquers Inca empire for Spain.

1534–36   Jacques Cartier of France in two voyages discovers St. Lawrence River and lands on site of Montreal.

1540   Francisco Coronado—searching for gold and the "Seven Cities of Cibola," explores American southwest.

1541 FRANCISCO DE ORELLANA JOURNEYS FROM THE HEADWATERS OF THE AMAZON RIVER TO THE ATLANTIC OCEAN.

1541   Hernando de Soto discovers the Mississippi River.

1595 CORNELIUS HOUTMAN LEADS DUTCH EXPEDITION FROM HOLLAND TO JAVA.

1600	Shakespeare begins ten-year period of writing his most famous plays.
1607	Captain John Smith leads first permanent English settlement at Jamestown, Virginia.
1609	Henry Hudson sails the Half Moon into New York Harbor, thence up the Hudson River to Albany.
1609	French explorer, Samuel de Champlain, discovers Lake Champlain.
1609	Spaniards settle Santa Fe, New Mexico.

1613 FATHER PAEZ SEEKS THE SOURCE OF THE BLUE NILE.

1619 JAN PIETERSZOON COEN CAPTURES DJAKARTA, JAVA, AND OBTAINS VALUABLE COMMERCIAL PRIVILEGES.

1619	First slaves brought to America at Jamestown, Virginia.
1620	Pilgrims leave Plymouth, England, on Mayflower for the New World.
1626	Peter Minuit buys Manhattan Island from the Indians for $24.00 worth of trinkets.
1682	Lower Mississippi River country claimed for France by Robert Cavelier sieur de La Salle.
1741	Alaska discovered by Captain Vitus Bering while exploring for Russia's Peter the Great.
1754	French and Indian War begins.
1755	Great earthquake kills 60,000 people in Lisbon, Portugal.

1768–71 CAPTAIN JAMES COOK EMBARKS ON FIRST EXPLORATION OF THE SOUTH PACIFIC.

1769	Napoleon Bonaparte born at Ajaccio, Corsica, on August 15.

1768–73 JAMES BRUCE EXPLORES TROPICAL AFRICA.

1772–75 CAPTAIN JAMES COOK SAILS ON SECOND VOYAGE OF EXPLORATION IN THE SOUTH PACIFIC.

1773	Boston Tea Party.

1774   First Continental Congress met at Philadelphia.
1775   American Revolutionary War begins with Battle of Lexington, April 19.
1775   Battle of Bunker Hill, June 17.

1776–79 CAPTAIN JAMES COOK UNDERTAKES THIRD AND LAST VOYAGE THROUGH OCEANIA.

1776   Declaration of Independence, July 4.
1777   Major General John Burgoyne surrenders to the Colonials at Saratoga, October 17.
1778   France recognizes independence of the thirteen American colonies—signs treaty of assistance February 6.
1779   John Paul Jones aboard *Bonhomme Richard* defeats English warship *Serapis* September 23.
1783   England recognizes independence and signs treaty of peace with new American nation, September 3.
1789   French Revolution.

1795–97 MUNGO PARK PENETRATES DARKEST AFRICA SEEKING MOUTH OF NIGER RIVER.

1796   President George Washington delivers farewell address, September 14.
1797   France orders all neutral ships carrying cargo for Great Britain to be captured.

1799–1804 ALEXANDER VON HUMBOLDT EXPLORES AMAZON TROPICS.

1805 MUNGO PARK ON SECOND EXPEDITION THROUGH TROPICAL AFRICA. WHILE SEEKING MOUTH OF NIGER RIVER, IS DROWNED IN ATTEMPT TO ESCAPE ATTACKING NATIVES.

1807   Robert Fulton makes first practical steamboat voyage in Clermont, August 17–22.
1812   United States and England engage in War.
1823   Monroe Doctrine declared, December 2.

1830–31 RICHARD LEMON LANDER AND BROTHER FIND THE MOUTH OF THE NIGER RIVER.

**1831 CHARLES DARWIN EMBARKS ABOARD THE BEAGLE FOR AN EX-
TENDED JOURNEY THROUGH THE TROPICS.**

1836   Siege of the Alamo, February 23–March 6.

1837   Victoria, age 18, becomes Queen of England.

1838–42   Antarctic islands found by Commander Charles Wilkes of the United States.

1844   Telegraph invented by Samuel F. B. Morse.

1846   United States–Mexican War, May 13.

1848   Gold discovered in California.

1848–52 ALFRED WALLACE JOURNEYS THROUGH THE AMAZON JUNGLE.

1851   Gold found in Australia.

1851   Cornerstones on the wings of the U. S. capitol building are laid.

1852   Louis Napoleon crowned emperor of France.

1849 DR. DAVID LIVINGSTONE BEGINS EXPLORING EQUATORIAL AFRICA.

1854–62 ALFRED RUSSEL WALLACE EXPLORES THE MALAY ARCHIPELAGO.

1854   Republican Party started at Ripon, Wisconsin, February 28.

1856   First railroad in California built.

1857   Cyrus W. Field lays first cable between Nova Scotia and Newfoundland.

1854–58 SIR RICHARD BURTON AND JOHN SPEKE BEGIN EXPLORING TROPICAL AFRICA FOR THE ROYAL GEOGRAPHIC SOCIETY.

1858   First Atlantic cable completed between England and America by Cyrus W. Field.

1859   First successful oil well drilled at Titusville, Pennsylvania.

1859   John Brown, abolitionist, hanged for raid on Harper's Ferry, Virginia.

1860 JOHN SPEKE, JOURNEYING THROUGH TROPICAL AFRICA, FINDS TRUE SOURCE OF THE NILE RIVER.

1860   Abraham Lincoln elected President of the United States.

1860–61   Pony express started between Sacramento, California and St. Joseph, Missouri.

1860   South Carolina secedes from the Union, December 20.

1861–64 SAMUEL BAKER AND WIFE FIND LAKE ALBERT AND MURCHISON FALLS IN EQUATORIAL AFRICA.

1861   Civil War begins in the United States.

1861   Fort Sumter surrenders, April 14.

1861   Battle of Bull Run.

1862   Naval engagement between the *Monitor* and the *Merrimack*.

1863   President Abraham Lincoln issues Emancipation Proclamation, January 1.

1863   Battle of Gettysburg.

1864   General Sherman marches through Georgia to the sea.

1865   General Lee surrenders to General Grant at Appomattox, April 9. Civil War ends.

1865   President Abraham Lincoln assassinated; dies April 15.

1864 FATHER DAMIEN COMES TO HAWAIIAN ISLANDS; BEGINS TO WORK AMONG THE LEPERS (1873).

1871 HENRY MORTON STANLEY FINDS DR. LIVINGSTONE, PRESUMED LOST IN EQUATORIAL AFRICA.

1871   Treaty of Frankfort ends Franco-Prussian War.

1873   Bank failures cause panic in New York City.

1874 HENRY MORTON STANLEY STARTS EXPLORATIONS IN TROPICAL AFRICA.

1876   General George A. Custer and 265 soldiers of the Seventh Cavalry killed June 25 in Battle of the Little Big Horn.

1877   Russia declares war on Turkey.

1881   Alexander II, Czar of Russia, assassinated.

1883   Professor Robert Koch of Germany announces the discovery of the TB germ.

1887   Flood in China kills 900,000 people.

1894–95   Chinese-Japanese War.

1895   X-rays discovered by William Roentgen, German physicist.

1896   Radioactivity of uranium discovered by A. H. Becquerel, of Paris.

1897–99   IN THE COURSE OF RESEARCH, DR. RONALD ROSS FINDS THE CAUSE OF TROPICAL MALARIA.

1898   Radium discovered by Pierre Curie, Mme. Curie and G. Bemont at Paris.

1898   Spanish-American War starts.

1899   South African (Boer) War starts.

1900   DR. WALTER REED AND COLLEAGUES FIND THE CAUSE OF YELLOW FEVER.

1901   President William McKinley shot, September 6— died on September 14.

1903   First successful heavier-than-air flight by the Wright Brothers.

1904–05   Russo-Japanese War.

1909   Admiral Robert E. Peary reaches North Pole, April 6.

1911   Captain Roald Amundsen reaches the North Pole, December 14.

1912   Titanic sinks; more than 1,500 passengers drown.

1913   URANIUM DISCOVERED IN THE REPUBLIC OF THE CONGO.

1913   DR. ALBERT SCHWEITZER ARRIVES IN TROPICAL AFRICA TO BEGIN HIS HUMANITARIAN WORK AMONG THE NATIVES.

1914   First ship passes through the Panama Canal.

1914   First World War begins with the assassination of Archduke Francis Ferdinand.

1915   Submarine warfare starts.

1916   Series of great land and sea battles—Verdun, Jutland Naval Battle—Battle of the Somme.

1917   United States enters World War I, April 6.

1917	Russian Revolution begins.
1918	World War I ends, November 11, at 11 A.M.
1920	League of Nations first meeting at Geneva, Switzerland, January 10.
1920	Nineteenth Amendment goes into effect; gives American women the right to vote.
1933	Adolf Hitler made German Chancellor, January 30.
1939	World War II commences.
1941	Japanese attack Pearl Harbor; United States plunged into World War II.
1945	First atomic bomb exploded at Alamogordo, N. M., July 16.
1945	Atom bomb dropped on Hiroshima, August 6—on Nagasaki, August 9.
1945	World War II ends.
1946	Republic of the Philippines becomes independent nation, July 4.
1948	Burma becomes independent nation, January 4.
1950–53	Korean War.
1953	Stalin dies, March 5.
1954	Cambodia joins family of independent nations, November 9.
1957	Sputnik I—first man-made satellite launched by Soviet scientists, October 4.
1958	Explorer I—first U.S. artificial satellite launched into space, January 31.
1958	Republic of Senegal gains independence.

1959 DR. L. S. B. LEAKEY FINDS ZINJANTHROPUS IN EAST AFRICA— ONE OF MAN'S EARLIEST ANCESTORS.

1959	Hawaiian Islands made 50th State.
1959	Soviet Lunik II photographs moon's far side.
1960	Belgian Congo becomes the Republic of Congo, June 30.
1960	Republic of Chad proclaims independence, August 11.

1960   Malagasy Republic (formerly Madagascar) gains independence, June 25.

1960   Republic of Dahomey (Africa) achieves independence August 1.

1961   Soviet astronaut, Major Yuri Gagarin, becomes first space traveler in Vostok I, April 12.

1962   Tanganyika becomes independent, December 9.

1962   Colonel John H. Glenn is first American astronaut to orbit the earth—three times February 20.

1962   Burundi (Africa) achieves independence, July 14.

1962   Island of Jamaica gains independence after 307 years of British rule.

INDEX